Measuring Up™ to the Ohio Learning Outcomes

and Success Strategies for the Ohio Proficiency Test

Reading

This book is customized for Ohio and the lessons match the **Ohio Learning Outcomes**. The Measuring Up™ program includes comprehensive worktexts and Ohio Diagnostic Practice Tests which are available separately.

800-822-1080
www.OHStandardsHelp.com

Peoples Publishing Group
299 Market Street, Saddle Brook, NJ 07663

Acknowledgements

Pg. 12, "Thornbush" Reprinted by permissions of Cricket Magazine, Feb. 2000, Vol. 27, No. 6, Copyright © 2000 by Carrel Muller; pg. 25, "Eleven" by Sandra Cisneros, Copyright © Sandra Cisneros 1989, from *The Sky Has Little Eyes*, published by Random House; pg. 31, "Water from the Well" Reprinted by permission of Cricket Magazine, April 2000, Copyright © 2000 by Uma Krishnaswami; pg. 38, "Sarah Tops" from *The Key Word and Other Mysteries* by Isaac Asimov, Copyright © 1977 by Isaac Asimov. Reprinted by permission of Walker and Company; pg. 51, "The Playoffs" by Linda Chiara, Boy's Life, April 2000, published by the Boy Scouts of America, Irving, TX, Copyright © 2000; pg. 66, "Poogweese" A Northwest Coast Indian folktale, retold by Chief Lelooska, Muse Magazine, 1999, Copyright © 1999, published by Carus Publishing Company; pg. 71, "The Golden Apples" by Mary Pope Osborne from *Favorite Norse Myths*, Copyright © 1996, published by Scholastic, Inc.; pg. 84, "The Potter and the Washerman" by Pam Hopper, Copyright © 1998 by Highlights for Children, Inc. Columbus Ohio; pg. 90, "Brothers on Ice" by Donna Gamache, published by Cricket Magazine, March 2000, Vol. 27, No. 71, Copyright © 2000 by Danna Gamache, Reprinted by permission of the author; pg. 101, *Tinkers Tide* by Marcy Barack, Copyright © 1998 Highlights for Children, Inc. Columbus, Ohio; pg. 110, "Wind Pictures" from *Winds* by Mary O'Neill, Copyright © 1970 Mary O'Neill, Copyright © renewed 1998 Abigail Hagler and Erin Baroni; pg. 121, "My Brother Bert" from MEET THE FOLKS by Ted Hughes, published by The Bobbs-Merrill Company, Inc. Copyright © 1961, 1973 by Ted Hughes; pg. 128, "Pigeons" from *Rainbow Writing* by Eve Merriam, Copyright © 1976 Eve Merriam; pg. 131, "Simile: Willow and Ginkgo" from *A Full Sky of Poems* by Eve Merriam, Copyright © 1964, 1970, 1973 by Eve Merriam. All rights reserved. Reprinted by permission of Marian Reiner for the author; pg. 134, "December Leaves" from *Don't Ever Cross a Crocodile* by Kay Starbird. Copyright © 1963 Kaye Starbird, Copyright c renewed 1991 Kaye Starbird; pg. 136, "Tuning Up" from *I Hear You Smiling and Other Poems* by Felice Holman, Charles Scribner's Sons Copyright © 1973; pg. 139, "The Pedalling Man" by Russell Hoban from *The Pedalling Man*, Heinemann, 1969; pg. 143, "The Grass" by Emily Dickinson; pg. 148, "Monopoly" from *Keepers* by Alice Schertle, Copyright © 1966 by Alice Schertle; pg. 152, "Thomas Jefferson" from *A Book of Americans* by Rosemary and Stephen Vincent Benet, published by Rinehart & Company, Inc. Copyright © 1933 by Rosemary and Stephen Vincent Benet; pg. 160, "The Way through the Woods" by Rudyard Kipling from *Rewards and Fairies* published by Doubleday & Company; pg. 165, "Someone" from *Collected Poems 1901-1918* by Walter de la Mare, Copyright © 1920 by Henry Holt and Company, Copyright © 1948 by Walter de la Mare; pg. 171, "How to Tell the Wild Animals" by Carolyn Wells, published by Dodd, Mead & Company; pg. 186, "The Woman Pharaoh" by Jean Malone, Reprinted with the permission of Archaeology's Dig Magazine, Aug/Sep 1999, Vol. 1 # 3, Copyright © Archaeological Institute of America; pg. 200, "Can Koalas Survive?" by Renee Skelton, National Geographic World, August 2000, Copyright © 2000 National Geographic Society; pg. 208, "Greeces' Glorious Games" by Stephen Hanks, Reprinted with the permission of Archaeology's Dig Magazine, Aug/Sep 2000, Copyright © Archaeological Institute of America; pg. 217, "Invasion of the Jellies" by Dewey Gram, published by Boy's Life, June 2000; pg. 221, "Ready, Set, Rescue" by Luba Vangelova, National Geographic World, National Geographic Society; pg. 226, "A Quest for Better Vision: Spectacles Over the Centuries" by Clara Hemphill, published by New York Times, August 8, 2000; pg. 241, "Making Faces" by Leslie Birdwell, Reprinted with the permission of Archaeology's Dig Magazine, Aug/Sep 2000, Vol. 2 # 4, Copyright © Archaeological Institute of America, Copyright © 2000; pg. 251, "The History of Counting" Copyright © 1999 by Denise Schmandt-Besserat, published by Morrow Junior Books, a division of William Morrow and Company, Inc.; pg. 260, "Say Hey! Who's the Best?" by Robert E. Hood, published by Boy's Life, August 2000.

Editorial Development, e2 Publishing Services
Pre-Press & Production Manager, Doreen Smith
Project Manager, Jason Grasso
Production Editor, Anna Rose Waider
Designer, Jason Grasso
Copy Editor, Lee Laddy, Gregory Ludwig
Proofreader, Amy Kron
Photo Researcher/Permissions Manager, Kristine Liebman
Illustrators, Armando Baéz, Jason Grasso
Cover Design, Armando Baéz

ISBN 1-56256-502-8

The Peoples Publishing Group, Inc.
299 Market Street
Saddle Brook, New Jersey 07663

Printed in the United States of America.

10 9 8 7 6

Dear Student,

What an exciting year you have in front of you. It is a year in which you will demonstrate your mastery of the Ohio Learning Outcomes for Reading.

The Ohio Proficiency Test measures your ability to comprehend fiction, poetry, and nonfiction. You show your ability by answering multiple-choice questions and writing responses to questions.

This book is designed to help you master the standards and be successful on the test. It provides:

- **A variety of interesting and informative model reading selections**

  When you read these narrative and informative selections, you will apply your before, during, and after reading strategies that help you to read independently.

- **Skill Builder lessons**

  These lessons provide instruction and practice for the standards. Look for the logo Skill Builder.

- **Apply to the Test**

  At the end of each Skill Builder, you will find Apply to the Test. It gives you practice for the skill in the same format as the test.

- **Independent Practice for the Test**

  This lesson asks you to take a sample test. Your confidence will grow as you become familiar with the test format.

Now it's time to get started. If you put your mind to it, by the time you finish this book, you will have mastered the standards and be ready for the test. We wish you a successful year.

Dear Caregiver,

The Ohio Learning Outcomes provide a definition of what each student should know. In Grade 6, mastery of these standards for reading is measured in March by the Ohio Proficiency Test.

Measuring Up to the Ohio Learning Outcomes is designed to help your child master the standards for reading and do well on the test. It provides instruction and practice in the standards as well as preparation for the test. To help your child be successful, it includes:

- **A variety of interesting and informative model reading selections**

  When students read these narrative and informative selections, they will apply their before, during, and after reading strategies. These strategies help them become independent readers.

- **Skill Builder lessons**

  These lessons provide instruction and practice for the standards. Look for the logo SkillBuilder.

- **Apply to the Test**

  At the end of each SkillBuilder is a feature called Apply to the Test. This feature provides practice for the skill in the same format as the test.

- **Independent Practice for the Test**

  This lesson provides a sample test. Your son or daughter's confidence will grow as he or she becomes familiar with the test format.

Reading is an essential skill for success in the real world. This book is not easy, but neither is the reading test. Ohio expects its students to measure up to the standards and to be able to demonstrate their mastery of these standards.

Your involvement is a crucial factor in your child's success. Here are some things you can do to help your child be successful.

- Show that you consider your son or daughter's success in school important. Each day, discuss what happened in school. Post successful compositions and tests on the refrigerator. Mark dates for tests on the calendar. Celebrate when your child does well.
- Provide a quiet place and a set time for homework. Help your son or daughter think through the assignments. Look them over before they are turned in. Of course, this doesn't mean do them but it does mean provide help and support.
- Show that you think reading is important. Let your son or daughter see you read and enjoy books. If your child doesn't have a library card, get one. Visit bookstores together. Attend book talks or readings with authors at your local library or bookstore.
- Keep magazines and newspapers around the house. Surf the Internet together. Look for articles about topics that interest you. Look for answers to questions.

I look forward to working with you this year to ensure your child's success. If you have any question, please do not hesitate to get in touch with me.

Table of Contents

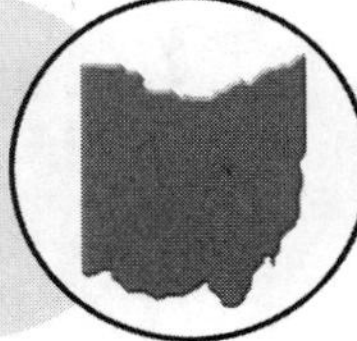

The lessons are aligned 100% to the Ohio Learning Outcomes!

Table of Contents

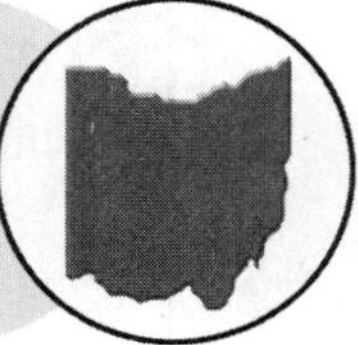

The lessons are aligned 100% to the Ohio Learning Outcomes!

Table of Contents

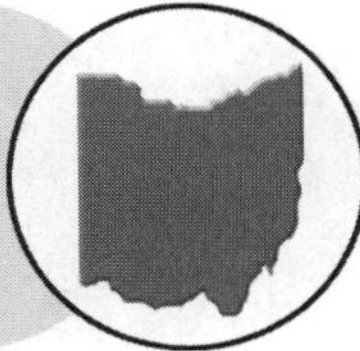

Table of Contents

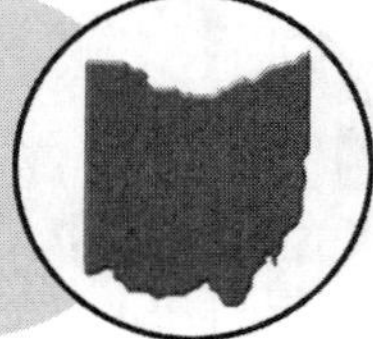

The lessons are aligned 100% to the Ohio Learning Outcomes!

This workbook is 100% aligned to the Ohio Learning Outcomes and provides complete practice for the Ohio Proficiency Test!

As each lesson is completed, place a check mark to indicate mastery or review needed.

Chapter 1: Reading Fiction for Literary Experience

Ohio Learning Outcomes																							
Review Needed																							
Mastery																							
Lessons	1	2	3	4	5	6	7	8	9	10	11	12	13	14	15	16	17	18	19	20	21	22	23
Given a fiction/poetry text to read silently, learners will demonstrate an understanding of language and elements of fiction/poetry by responding to items in which they:																							
1 analyze aspects of the text, examining, for example, characters, setting, plot, problem/solution, point of view, or theme		●	●		●	●	●	●	●			●	●				●	●			●		
2 summarize the text		●												●			●						
3 infer from the text		●	●						●						●		●	●			●		
4 respond to the text		●	●							●	●						●	●	●	●	●		
Given a fiction/poetry text to read silently, learners will demonstrate an understanding of language and elements of fiction/poetry by responding to items in which they:																							
5 compare and contrast aspects of the text, for example, characters or settings																		●					
6 critique and evaluate the text										●	●							●	●				
7 select information for a variety of purposes, including enjoyment	●																					●	●
8 express reasons for recommending or not recommending the text for a particular audience or purpose																							●
9 explain how an author uses contents of a text to support his/her purpose for writing.	●	●																					
Given a nonfiction text to read silently, learners will demonstrate an understanding of language and elements of nonfiction by responding to items in which they:																							
10 analyze the text, examining, for example, author's use of comparison and contrast, cause and effect, or fact and opinion																							
11 summarize the text																							
12 infer from the text																							
13 respond to the text																							
Given a nonfiction text to read silently, learners will demonstrate an understanding of language and elements of nonfiction by responding to items in which they:																							
14 compare and/or contrast aspects of the text																							
15 critique and evaluate the text for such elements as organizational structure and logical reasoning																							
16 select information from a variety of resources to support ideas, concepts, and interpretations																							
17 express reasons for recommending or not recommending the text for a particular audience or purpose																							
18 explain how an author uses contents of a text to support his/her purpose for writing																							

This workbook is 100% aligned to the Ohio Learning Outcomes and provides complete practice for the Ohio Proficiency Test!

As each lesson is completed, place a check mark to indicate mastery or review needed.

Chapter 2: Reading Poetry

Ohio Learning Outcomes	1	2	3	4	5	6	7	8	9	10	11	12	13	14	15	16	17	18	19
Review Needed	☐	☐	☐	☐	☐	☐	☐	☐	☐	☐	☐	☐	☐	☐	☐	☐	☐	☐	☐
Mastery	☐	☐	☐	☐	☐	☐	☐	☐	☐	☐	☐	☐	☐	☐	☐	☐	☐	☐	☐
Given a fiction/poetry text to read silently, learners will demonstrate an understanding of language and elements of fiction/poetry by responding to items in which they:																			
1 analyze aspects of the text, examining, for example, characters, setting, plot, problem/solution, point of view, or theme		●	●				●	●					●				●		
2 summarize the text	●	●						●						●			●		
3 infer from the text		●	●				●						●	●	●		●		
4 respond to the text		●						●	●					●	●	●	●	●	●
Given a fiction/poetry text to read silently, learners will demonstrate an understanding of language and elements of fiction/poetry by responding to items in which they:																			
5 compare and contrast aspects of the text, for example, characters or settings		●			●		●					●					●		
6 critique and evaluate the text						●						●							
7 select information for a variety of purposes, including enjoyment	●																		
8 express reasons for recommending or not recommending the text for a particular audience or purpose									●			●	●						●
9 explain how an author uses contents of a text to support his/her purpose for writing.	●	●								●		●							
Given a nonfiction text to read silently, learners will demonstrate an understanding of language and elements of nonfiction by responding to items in which they:																			
10 analyze the text, examining, for example, author's use of comparison and contrast, cause and effect, or fact and opinion																			
11 summarize the text																			
12 infer from the text																			
13 respond to the text																			
Given a nonfiction text to read silently, learners will demonstrate an understanding of language and elements of nonfiction by responding to items in which they:																			
14 compare and/or contrast aspects of the text																			
15 critique and evaluate the text for such elements as organizational structure and logical reasoning																			
16 select information from a variety of resources to support ideas, concepts, and interpretations																			
17 express reasons for recommending or not recommending the text for a particular audience or purpose																			
18 explain how an author uses contents of a text to support his/her purpose for writing																			

This workbook is 100% aligned to the Ohio Learning Outcomes and provides complete practice for the Ohio Proficiency Test!

As each lesson is completed, place a check mark to indicate mastery or review needed.

Chapter 3: Reading Nonfiction

Ohio Learning Outcomes	1	2	3	4	5	6	7	8	9	10	11	12	13	14	15	16	17	18	19	20	21	22	23
Review Needed																							
Mastery																							
Given a fiction/poetry text to read silently, learners will demonstrate an understanding of language and elements of fiction/poetry by responding to items in which they:																							
1 analyze aspects of the text, examining, for example, characters, setting, plot, problem/solution, point of view, or theme																							
2 summarize the text																							
3 infer from the text																							
4 respond to the text																							
Given a fiction/poetry text to read silently, learners will demonstrate an understanding of language and elements of fiction/poetry by responding to items in which they:																							
5 compare and contrast aspects of the text, for example, characters or settings																							
6 critique and evaluate the text																							
7 select information for a variety of purposes, including enjoyment																							
8 express reasons for recommending or not recommending the text for a particular audience or purpose																							
9 explain how an author uses contents of a text to support his/her purpose for writing.																							
Given a nonfiction text to read silently, learners will demonstrate an understanding of language and elements of nonfiction by responding to items in which they:																							
10 analyze the text, examining, for example, author's use of comparison and contrast, cause and effect, or fact and opinion		●	●		●	●	●			●	●												
11 summarize the text		●						●			●							●			●		
12 infer from the text		●							●	●	●												
13 respond to the text		●									●	●						●	●	●	●		●
Given a nonfiction text to read silently, learners will demonstrate an understanding of language and elements of nonfiction by responding to items in which they:																							
14 compare and/or contrast aspects of the text		●			●								●								●		
15 critique and evaluate the text for such elements as organizational structure and logical reasoning		●											●	●									●
16 select information from a variety of resources to support ideas, concepts, and interpretations	●																					●	
17 express reasons for recommending or not recommending the text for a particular audience or purpose															●							●	
18 explain how an author uses contents of a text to support his/her purpose for writing	●	●														●							

Chapter 1 Reading Fiction for Literary Experience

What's Coming Up?

In this chapter, you will learn:

- what fiction is
- strategies and skills for reading fiction
- how to analyze words
- how to analyze characters
- how to analyze setting
- how to analyze plot
- how to analyze problems and solutions
- how to write a short response
- how to analyze point of view
- how to analyze theme
- how to summarize
- how to make inferences
- how to build vocabulary
- how to apply what you have learned to the test
- how to write an extended response

Does This Sound Familiar?

- You're reading a novel that's so good you just can't put it down. You keep turning the pages to find out what happens next.
- It's a special occasion, such as your birthday or graduation. Your family is celebrating by going out to dinner and attending a performance of a play.
- You settle into your seat in your social studies class. Your teacher begins the class by reading aloud. Today she's reading a Native American legend.
- You go to the bookstore. As you're browsing through the shelves in the young adult section, you see that an author you enjoy has published a new collection of short stories.

Chapter 1 Reading Fiction for Literary Experience

Fiction is All Around You!

People who say they don't like to read probably never had the pleasure of getting their hands on a good book. A good story entertains you. Sometimes it keeps you turning pages, unable to stop, until you get to the ending. A good book can be like a good friend. You laugh and cry with it and the characters seem like real people, so real that you seem to know them. Perhaps you have read *Hatchet* by Gary Paulsen, *Harry Potter* by J.K. Rowlings, or some of the books in the *Animorphs* series by K.A. Applegate. No matter what kind of reader you are, set a time soon to check out the bookstore or your library for the newest bestsellers. Surely something will catch your eye, something that will get you hooked on reading.

Activity

Directions Think about what makes fiction enjoyable and fun to read. Work with a partner and make a list of five things you like to find in a good book, short story, or play. Consider the type of characters you enjoy reading about, plots and settings that keep you interested, and themes that you relate to.

1. What do the characters like to do.
2. Where the story takes place
3. How do the characters react to the promble
4. Who wrote the story?
5. How the charcacters treat each other.

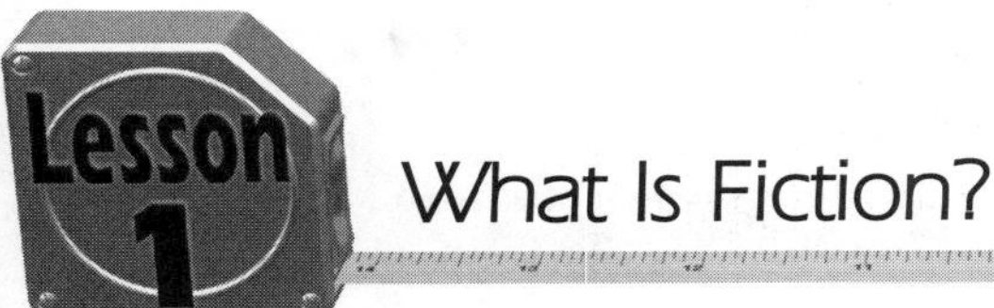

What Is Fiction?

Fiction Is...

Fiction is imaginative literature. It is a story that is born from a writer's imagination.

Realistic Fiction
In realistic fiction, the characters are imaginary people but their actions and conversations are true-to-life. Although the story is made-up, the events could theoretically happen and the setting could actually exist. The story, however, is an imaginary one.

Historical Fiction
Some stories are based on people, places, or events from history. This is historical fiction. A story about a real boy who lived in Georgia during the Civil War would be classified as historical fiction.

Fantasy
A fantasy is an imaginary story that could never actually happen. The characters may be fantastical or they may have special powers, such as the ability to read people's minds. In a fantasy, the events could never really happen and/or the places in the story don't really exist. There are always elements in a fantasy that are not based on reality.

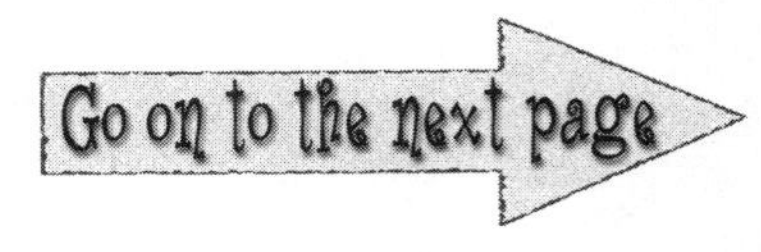

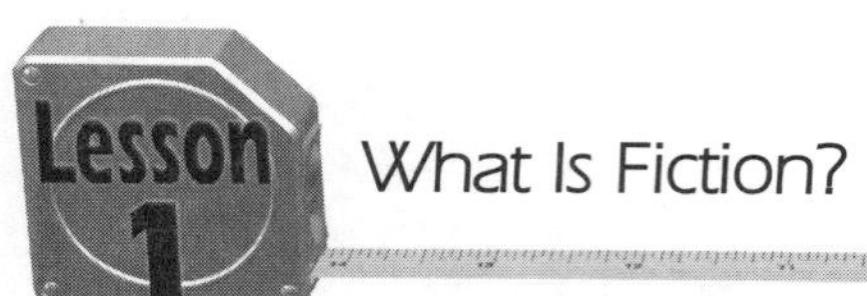

Lesson 1 What Is Fiction?

Types of Fiction

Short Stories A short story is exactly what its name suggests. It is a short piece of fiction that focuses on a particular event or series of events that happen over a short period of time. A short story focuses on one or a limited number of characters. The length of a short story makes it possible to read during a brief period of time.

Novels A novel is a long fictional work. The story may take place over a short or long period of time. The main characters will be fully developed through the events of the story and the dialogue they engage in. Novels are usually divided into chapters.

Myths, Legends, Folktales These are stories from the past that may have different versions and have been handed down by word of mouth. Myths are old stories that most often explain something about nature. They are stories that may explain about things such as life and death, lightening, or the changes of the seasons. Gods and goddesses are frequently the characters in myths. A legend is also a story brought down by word of mouth, but it focuses on the great deeds of heroes. The stories of Robin Hood and King Arthur are legends. Folktales are tales retold over many years that have simple characters and simple conflicts that are resolved at the very end of the story.

Drama Drama is the study of a play. A play is a story that is meant to be performed or read aloud. The parts of the characters are acted out for an audience and the story is told through their actions and dialogue.

Electronic Books Books can be found on CD-ROMs. A CD-ROM can allow you to interact with the story by making the characters move, choosing the next event in the plot, or by defining difficult words.

Special Text Features of Fiction

Fiction has special features that sets it apart from other types of writing. These include:

Chapters: Long fictional works such as novels are usually divided into shorter segments called chapters. Chapters may have numbers or titles. The chapter titles may provide a clue to what the chapter will be about.

Dialogue: Characters come alive in fiction through dialogue. Dialogue is the conversations that the characters have. Much of what you get to know about a character, you find out through what he or she says. Dialogue is set off from the rest of the text with quotation marks.

Illustrations for novels and short stories: Illustrations or pictures may accompany novels and short stories. Illustrations help to break up the text and depict the characters, setting, or events of the story.

Cast of Characters: At the beginning of a play, you will find a cast of characters. The names of the characters are listed and often a brief description of how the character is related to another character is given.

Stage Directions: Stage directions in drama give important background information, such as where actors should stand and what should be happening.

Dialogue for Drama: Every time a character says something in a play, the words are preceded by the name of the character. If you are reading a play aloud, you need to pay attention so that you know which character is speaking and when it is your turn to say your character's lines.

Go on to the next page

What Is Fiction?

Purpose for Reading Fiction

You may have different purposes for reading fiction. You may read fiction

- for your own entertainment and to **enjoy** a good story.
- to **understand** more about life, people, experiences, or events.
- to **find out** about the lives of characters and how their lives relate to you.
- to understand how characters **solve problems** that may be similar to problems that you have experienced.

Rate

Your reading rate is how quickly or slowly you read a text. The rate at which you read a story often depends on your purpose for reading it.

- Read slowly if
  - the plot of the text is difficult to follow.
  - the dialogue is difficult to understand.
  - the vocabulary is unfamiliar.
  - you will need to answer questions about what you have read.
  - you will be taking a test based on the text.
- Read at a comfortable pace if
  - you are reading for your own pleasure.
  - the plot and dialogue is easy to follow.
  - the text is not full of complicated ideas or difficult vocabulary.

Activity

A. **Directions** Fill in the chart by writing the titles of different fiction that you have enjoyed reading. Then write a brief summary about each one.

TITLE	SUMMARY
Danger Boy	I liked Danger Boy because it had a kid from the future use a time machine to try to get his mom back to the future.
Trapped	I liked trapped because it had a pig falling out of a truck and a kids save it while a cat is trying to bust the [illegible].

B. **Directions** Read each situation below and answer the question.

1. Your favorite mystery writer just came out with a new book. Why would you read this book?

Because I like mystery books and want to see another from my favorite writer.

2. Your teacher said that your class is going to read a short story. The story focuses on a problem that your own community is experiencing. Why might your teacher want the class to read this story?

So that maybe some students will help out with the problem.

3. Your family has tickets to see the play *Romeo and Juliet* by William Shakespeare. Why would you read the play before you see the play?

Because I would want to see the cast and the dialogue.

Lesson 2 How to Read Fiction

Reading is not a passive activity. To get the most out of what you read, follow these keys to success.

Keys TO Success

APPLY READING STRATEGIES

Set a Purpose

Before you begin reading anything, you should have a purpose in mind for reading it. You may read for enjoyment, to learn about something, or to find out new information. If you know you that you will be tested on what you are reading, you will read with that purpose in mind.

Make, Confirm, and Revise Predictions

Part of the excitement of reading is making a prediction or logical guess about what may happen next. Do this by using your prior knowledge and clues from the story. As you continue reading, evaluate the prediction that you made. If a prediction is incorrect, you can revise it.

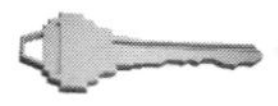

Retell

Retell a story or a passage that you have read by putting it into your own words. If you are able to retell a story, it is a good sign that you understand the story.

Summarize

Summarizing helps you to understand what you are reading. Stop every now and then, especially after reading a difficult passage or chapter, to summarize it or give a brief description of the main events. Do not include minor events or unimportant details.

Connect Important Ideas

Piece together important events and ideas as you read a story. Look closely at what a character is doing and saying and see how the story unfolds.

Link Ideas to Your Own Experience and Knowledge

Link your own experiences and prior knowledge to the story. See if any of your experiences, feelings, or ideas are similar to those of a character in the story.

Form Pictures

As you read, create a mental picture of what is happening. Visualize the places and people and let yourself be drawn into the story.

Check Your Understanding

Pause every now and then to make sure you understand what you have read. Ask yourself questions such as: Do I understand what happened? Do I understand what's behind this character's actions and motives? Am I realizing how one event is affecting another? Reread sections that have confused you. If necessary, look up difficult words in a dictionary.

Make Inferences

Since authors don't always explain everything, you'll need to fill in the gaps as you read. You'll need to make inferences or reasonable assumptions about characters' actions and behavior. By using clues from the story and your own knowledge, you can fill in the information that the author doesn't tell you.

Use Context Clues

When you come across an unfamiliar or difficult word, use context clues to help you figure out the word's meaning. The other words in the sentence or the ideas in the passage may help you to identify what the word means.

Go on to the next page

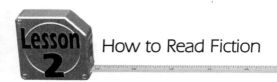

LOOK FOR ELEMENTS OF LITERATURE

Characters

The characters are the people or personified animals (animals with human qualities) in the story. You learn about who the characters are by their actions, behavior, physical appearance, and their words or conversations with other characters. When you analyze a character, you examine his or her feelings, emotions, goals, personality traits, and motives.

Setting

The setting is where and when the story takes place. When you analyze the setting of a story, you'll decide how important the setting is in that particular story. You'll also determine how the setting influences the characters and the events that take place.

Plot

The plot is the events that happen in a story. The events may occur in chronological order (time order) or they may be presented through flashbacks. A flashback is a scene from the past. Authors may also mix up events to pique your curiosity. For instance, a story may begin with what happened last and then go on to tell the events that led up to the episode described at the story's beginning.

As you analyze the plot, make sure that you understand the order of events. The sequence of events and the characters' actions are integral to understanding the story. Look also for the characters' problems. The story will usually end soon after the problems are solved and the conflict is resolved.

Problem/Solution

Central to the plot of a story is the problem and its solution. The problem can be a situation that the main character wants to change or something that the character wants to do or find out. The solution is the action or decision that makes it clear to the character how the problem can be solved. As you analyze the problem of a story, you will see how events fit together and what action is taken to bring about a solution.

Point of View

The point of view is the author's choice of narrator or speaker in the story. In first-person point of view, a character in the story tells the story. Pronouns such as *I*, *me*, *our*, or *my* give you clues that the story is being told in first-person. In third-person point of view, the author, not a character in the story, relates the events. Who is telling the story will determine how much is revealed about each character and event. When you analyze a story's point of view, consider why the author chose to write from this perspective and how the story would be different if the story was told from a different point of view.

Theme

The theme is the central meaning of the story. It is like a thread that runs through the story and holds it together. When you analyze a story to identify its theme, you will think about the overall message or major point about life that the author is trying to communicate. For instance, the theme in a story about a boy who discovers his roots may be *that it is important to know where you came from.*

Go on to the next page

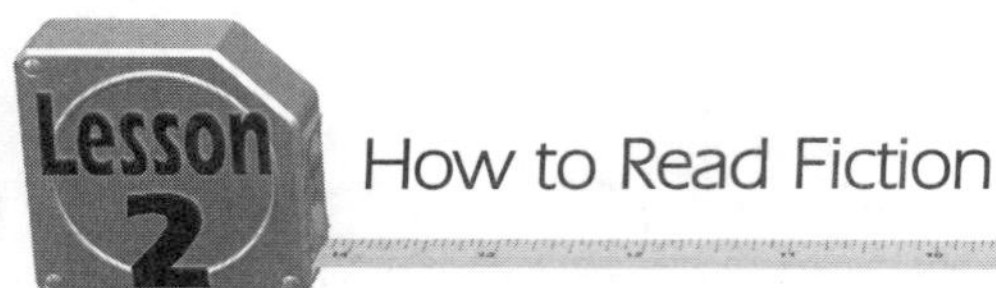

READING GUIDE

Directions Use the questions in the right-hand column to guide your reading.

Thornbush
—Carrel Muller

1 Thornbush grew near the path used by children to lead cattle from the village to pasture. It was a small thornbush, hardly a twig, but its thorns were long and sharp. One day while Nama was playing with the other
2 children, he stumbled, and a thorn pierced his side.

3 A year later Nama was taken to the men's compound to be taught the skills and ways of a warrior. He was quick in learning to shape his spear and he worked hard learning to throw straight. He learned well the chants, songs, and dances of a warrior. One lesson he learned and took to heart was that a warrior must perfect himself for battle. Carelessness could mean death. He did not wish to stumble and, through carelessness, fail. Then he remembered thornbush.

4 "It was long ago," said Old Man. "You were then a child. Do not concern yourself with thornbush."

But Nama could not forget. He again walked the children's path. "Thornbush, thornbush, you gave me pain," spoke Nama. "I will cut you down. You will not give pain ever again."

Thornbush whispered, "You cannot get rid of me. I am your pain. I am your strength."

Nama cut thornbush down. For a while Nama did not think or worry about thornbush. Then he heard the woman complaining.

"How did that thornbush grow so big?"

"It is scratching all who walk the path."

"Yes, the children and the cattle."

Nama again walked the children's path. There he found not the small thornbush, but a large one with great thorns. "Thornbush, thornbush," he spoke, "you grow stronger. I can bear your presence no longer."

Thornbush whispered, "You cannot get rid of me. I am your pain. I am your strength."

GUIDED QUESTIONS

1 **Form a picture of the path and the thornbrush in your mind. Describe what you think it looks like.**

2 **What is the setting of this story?**

3 **Using context clues, can you figure out what the word *compound* means?**

4 **From what point of view is this story told? How do you know?**

READING GUIDE

Nama cut down thornbush. But it grew again, larger and stronger, so Nama returned. "Thornbush, thornbush," I come with great rocks. I will cut you down, and under these stones you will be locked."

Thornbush whispered, "Though your heart be rent, under the earth I will not stay. I am your pain. I am your strength." And through the rocks thornbush returned and grew stronger.

Nama's heart was heavy. When he and the other boys practiced the warrior's dance, he could not run as fast or leap as high as the others.

Old Man spoke to him. "What is wrong? You are young. You are strong. What weighs you down?"

"It is thornbush. It keeps growing. It is important that I get rid of it."

5 Old Man nodded. "You have made it too big. Go get a thorn and make a pouch to carry it in."

Nama did this and tied the pouch around his waist with a leather thong. "How long must I wear this?" he asked.

"When you no longer need it, you will throw it away," said Old Man.

For a while all went well. Some days Nama could run and leap and toss his spear farther and faster than all others. Then some task would send him back along the children's path, and he would see thornbush.

I must get rid of it, or I will never be a warrior, thought Nama. He decided to poison thornbush. He had learned
6 poison for hunting —why not use his skill on thornbush?

He had just poured poison over the rocks where thornbush grew when a young girl carrying a water jug came running.

"Lioness," she shouted. "Cattle killed!" she panted.

Then others came running. All gathered and discussed the danger to the village. Tomorrow the men would go hunting for the lioness. The boys could follow at a distance but could not participate. Their initiation as warriors was not for another month.

GUIDED QUESTIONS

5 **Reflect on what the Old Man tells Nama and link his comment to your own experience. Do you agree that Nama has made his problem "too big"?**

6 **Stop here to summarize what you have read. What has happened so far?**

Go on to the next page

READING GUIDE

For days the warriors returned unsuccessful from the hunt. The lioness, though wounded, still roamed free, more dangerous than ever. Then the women complained, "We have now another fear. A poisonous snake is living in the rocks where thornbush grows."

Nama was heartsick. "Has my poison drawn a snake to the path? I must kill it. I will not follow the hunters today."

Nama went to the path. "Thornbush, I have made you strong. I have placed a snake at your roots. Today I will right this wrong."

Thornbush whispered, "I am your pain. I am your strength. Be brave!"

Slowly, cautiously, he began moving all the rocks he had so painfully gathered and placed on the spot where thornbush grew. The snake that slept under them rose angrily and spoke: "Who disturbs my home?"

7 "Snake, I, Nama have come to destroy your home and you."

Snake answered, "I am quick. I work hard. I know well the warrior's ways." It darted out and watched Nama, poised for attack.

Nama moved with care. He armed himself as a warrior. With knife and spear he prepared himself for battle.

Snake darted forward. Nama threw his knife. It glanced off a rock and fell harmlessly to the ground. Snake moved cautiously, quickly toward Nama, but it attacked the air, for Nama jumped clear. Once more Snake poised for attack. Nama struck swift and true. Snake writhed in pain and lay still, pinned to the earth with Nama's spear. With Snake dead at his feet, Nama gave the cry of a warrior, but since he was alone, it was not echoed by other hunters. He turned and walked to thornbush.

8 It seemed to whisper to him, "Beware! Be brave!"

Then Nama heard a noise in the bush. The sound trembled through the earth, up his feet, to the very top of
9 his head. He knew the sound: the low growl of the lioness! The hunted was now hunting him. He faced her as she stepped from the brush. His mind raced: I cannot look for my knife. I cannot turn my back to reach for my spear. I must not stumble or fail.

GUIDED QUESTIONS

7 **Stop here to check your understanding of the decision Nama makes and the consequences of his actions. Explain what happens.**

8 **What do you predict will happen next after the thornbush whispers to beware and to be brave?**

9 **What problem does Nama face? What is his solution?**

READING GUIDE

10 Nama reached out, never taking his eyes from the wounded lioness, and with both hands tore thornbush from the earth. The thorns stabbed his arms and chest, but he held thornbush, his only weapon against the wounded, dangerous, unpredictable foe. Her eyes flashing and her snarl vibrating the earth, she attacked. Nama jumped aside and swung thornbush. Sharp thorns tore at her face, and she cried in pain and fury. She turned quickly but now moved more cautiously, warily circling Nama, who dared not take his eyes from her.

Furiously, the lioness lunged toward Nama, who clutched thornbush in both hands to defend himself from her attack. As the lioness leaped, Nama thrust thornbush into her face. She screamed in pain as the thorns stabbed her eyes. Her claws reached out and tore down Nama's shoulders and chest, but Nama fought her with thornbush. A branch broke as he jammed it into her throat. She gasped, could not breathe, and slowly fell, claws still tearing at the warrior who struggled with her. As she fell, Nama grabbed his spear and, screaming the warrior's cry,
11 ended the suffering.

GUIDED QUESTIONS

10 **Analyze Nama as a character. What are his primary character traits?**

11 **Think about the story's plot. What events occur that turn the thornbush from a source of pain to a source of strength for Nama?**

Go on to the next page

READING GUIDE

Shouts of warriors echoed his cry as the men appeared around him. Soon women and children were running up the path. Then rejoicing began, for the danger was over and a new warrior was honored. At the initiation celebration Nama danced and enacted his battle, telling how he met and overcame lioness with thornbush. The thorns and claws left scars that could not be distinguished one from the other. These Nama wore as proudly as he wore the skin of the lioness over his shoulders, the signs of his first victory.

Nama became one of the bravest warriors of his village. He never again walked the path of children, so he never saw the pouch with one thorn that was lost in battle. He never saw the rocks scattered about marking the spot where once a thornbush grew. Thornbush was remembered only as a weapon and shield, as pain and strength in the
12 story of a great warrior.

GUIDED QUESTIONS

12 Explain how the line, "I am your pain. I am your strength." is a theme of the story.

Fluency Tip

We all make mistakes as we read. Sometimes we accidentally skip a line and realize that what we have read doesn't make sense. Other times we misread a phrase or word. We may even misunderstand what has happened in the plot or in a complicated dialogue. Anytime you feel that you have made a mistake, correct yourself. Stop, go back, and reread.

How to Answer Multiple-Choice Questions

What's Expected on the Test?

The Ohio Proficiency Test asks you to read fiction, poetry, and nonfiction selections and to answer questions about them. Some of the questions will be multiple-choice type questions. Other questions will require a short written response or even an extended or long response.

In this section you will concentrate on answering multiple-choice questions. A multiple-choice questions has two parts. The first part is the question stem. A number comes before the question. The second part is the choice. The choices will usually be labeled with letters. Your task is to choose the correct answer from these choices.

Test-Taking Strategies

Read Each Question Carefully

Read each question and look for words such as *only, all, not, except*, and *never*. These words affect the meaning of the question. Be aware of questions that ask you to find the *best* answer. In a question like this, some answers may not actually be wrong but only one answer is the best.

Keep Going

Don't spend too much time on any one question. You want to make sure that you have time to answer every question. Remember, you get just as much credit for answering easy questions as you do for answering difficult questions.

Go Back to the Text

Sometimes, the answer to a question is right there in the text. Notice the key words used in the question and the answer choices. Scan the story and look for those key words. When you find them, it will signal that you have pinpointed the right part of the text.

Eliminate Incorrect Choices

Sometimes you can get a question right simply by eliminating the wrong choices. Look for answers that seem obviously incorrect. If you can discount two of the four choices, then you have a fifty percent chance of choosing the right answer.

Double-check

As you complete each question, make sure that you have filled in the correct circle on your answer sheet. You can make a simple mistake by filling in B when you really meant to fill in C. If time allows, reread each question and double-check all of your answers.

How to Answer Multiple-Choice Questions

Sample Multiple-Choice Questions

Directions Try your hand at answering these multiple-choice questions about "Thornbush." Reread the story before you begin. After you have answered the questions, turn to page 19 to check your responses.

1. Which statement best expresses the theme of Thornbush?

A. Always cut down a thornbush when you see one.

B. Never trust a wild animal such as a lioness or a snake.

C. Scratches and wounds show that you are a true warrior.

D. You have to know your pain in order to achieve strength.

2. Why did the children walk along the path where the thornbush lay?

A. The children walked the path because they wanted to see the thornbush.

B. The children walked the path to lead cattle from the village to pasture.

C. The children used the path as a playground.

D. The children did not walk the path where the thornbush lay.

3. Why did Nama decide not to follow the hunters?

A. He wanted to kill the poisonous snake living where thornbush grew.

B. He needed to put more rocks on the place where thornbush grew.

C. He felt ill from the poison he placed on the ground near thornbush.

D. He had a feeling that he knew where he could find the lioness.

4. What happens after Nama kills the snake?

A. The thornbush attacks Nama.

B. The warriors come to congratulate Nama.

C. Nama makes a necklace from the snake's rattle.

D. Nama hears and sees the angry lioness.

5. What important event led Nama to becoming one of the bravest warriors of his village?

A. He killed the snake.

B. He put rocks where the thornbush grows.

C. He used the thornbush to fight the lioness.

D. He poisoned thornbush.

Check Your Answers Check your answers and the explanations below to understand which choices were correct and incorrect.

1. Which statement best expresses the theme of Thornbush?
   A. **INCORRECT** This is not a message that is communicated throughout the story.
   B. **INCORRECT** Although the lioness and snake are untrustworthy in the story, this is not the overall message of the story.
   C. **INCORRECT** A warrior's wounds is not a central idea in the story that is integral to the story's overall meaning.
   D. **CORRECT** This is an overall message that the author communicates.

2. Why did the children walk along the path where the thornbush lay?
   A. **INCORRECT** The story does not state this fact.
   B. **CORRECT** The story states in the first paragraph that the path was used by the children to lead the cattle from the village to the pasture.
   C. **INCORRECT** The story does not state this fact.
   D. **INCORRECT** The children did need to walk along this path.

3. Why did Nama decide not to follow the hunters?
   A. **CORRECT** The poisonous snake is the reason Nama does not go.
   B. **INCORRECT** Nama did this previously and this is not the reason that he doesn't join the hunters.
   C. **INCORRECT** This is not a true detail from the story.
   D. **INCORRECT** Nama did not know that he would find the lioness by the thornbush.

4. What happens after Nama kills the snake?
   - A. **INCORRECT** The thornbush tells Nama to beware. It never attacks him.
   - B. **INCORRECT** The warriors are not aware that Nama has killed the snake because they are elsewhere hunting for the lioness.
   - C. **INCORRECT** This is not a true detail from the story.
   - D. **CORRECT** Nama hears and sees the lioness.

5. What important event led Nama to becoming one of the bravest warriors of his village?
   - A. **INCORRECT** Although this required bravery and skill, it wasn't the key event that led to his success as a warrior.
   - B. **INCORRECT** This did not show Nama's bravery as a warrior.
   - C. **CORRECT** The result of Nama's fight with the lioness was his first victory as a brave warrior.
   - D. **INCORRECT** This action did not show Nama's skill or bravery as a warrior.

Word Analysis

Compound Words

A compound word is a word made up of two words that are joined together. Usually, you can figure out the meaning of the compound word if you know the meaning of the two individual words. For example, *afternoon* is the time of day that occurs after noon, or after 12:00 P.M. An *earring* is a ring or piece of jewelry that is worn on the ear.

Sometimes, however, the meaning of the compound word is less clearly related to the meaning of the two separate words. For instance, the word *outcome*, means *result*, or the way the situation turns out.

Activity

A. **Directions** Read these sentences from the story. Each underlined word is a compound word. Write a definition for each compound word on the line.

1. Do not concern yourself with thornbush.

____

2. Nama was heartsick.

____

3. I cannot look for my knife.

____

4. At the initiation celebration Nama danced and enacted his battle, telling how he met and overcame lioness with thornbush.

____

5. Nama cut the thornbush down.

____

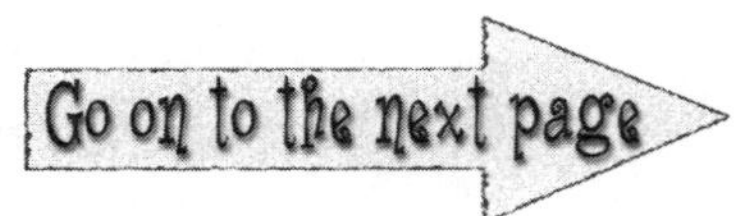

Activity continued

B. **Directions** Match each compound word with its definition. Write the letter of the correct matching word on the line.

________	**1.** headstrong	**a.** forest
________	**2.** overlook	**b.** determined to have one's way
________	**3.** buttercup	**c.** a small yellow flower
________	**4.** rattlesnake	**d.** a poisonous snake that makes a rattling sound
________	**5.** sunrise	**e.** fail to notice something
________	**6.** vineyard	**f.** stories that are passed down
________	**7.** undertake	**g.** an area of land for growing grapes
________	**8.** woodland	**h.** the time in the morning when the sun appears
________	**9.** tugboat	**i.** a powerful boat that pulls
________	**10.** folk stories	**j.** agree to do a job

C. **Directions** Draw lines to make compound words. Write the compound word on the line. Then write a short definition for each word.

List 1	List 2	Compound Word	Definition
look	board		
rail	back		
over	road		
flash	pass		
clip	out		

1. Which answer BEST explains what a compound words is?

   A. two words that work together to form a new word

   B. words with multiple syllables and multiple definitions

   C. two words that rhyme

   D. two unrelated words

2. Which of the following is a compound word?

   A. poisonous

   B. lioness

   C. dragonfly

   D. warrior

3. Which compound word means *one more*?

   A. another

   B. overlook

   C. nevertheless

   D. someone

Analyze Characters

Characters

Characters are the people or animals in the story. Sometimes even an object, such as the thornbush, can be a character. The most important or central character that the story revolves around is the main character.

Characters have character traits. These are the special qualities that an author gives the characters to make them come alive and seem like real people. Authors reveal what characters are like by describing how they look, dress, act, or feel. As you read, you can learn a lot about a character's personality by observing what a character says and how other characters react to him or her.

When you analyze a character, you figure out things such as if the character is brave, self-confident, shy, or quiet. You get to know what characters are good or weak at, and what they like or dislike. As you analyze characters, you get to know them.

In *Thornbush*, for instance, you can analyze Nama as a character. What can you figure out about him? He is persistent because he is determined to get rid of the thornbush. During his fight with the snake and the lioness, you learn that he is extremely brave and clever.

Activity **Directions** Read *Eleven* by Sandra Cisneros and answer the questions.

Eleven

—by Sandra Cisneros

What they don't understand about birthdays and what they never tell you is that when you're eleven, you're also ten, and nine, and eight, and seven, and six, and five, and four, and three, and two, and one. And when you wake up on your eleventh birthday you expect to feel eleven, but you don't. You open your eyes and everything's just like you're still ten. And you are—underneath the year that makes you eleven.

Like some days you might say something stupid, and that's the part of you that's still ten. Or maybe some days you might need to sit on your mama's lap because you're scared, and that's the part of you that's five. And one day when you're all grown up maybe you will need to cry like if you're three, and that's okay. That's what I tell Mama when she's sad and needs to cry. Maybe she's feeling three.

Because the way you grow old is kind of like an onion or like the rings inside a tree trunk or like my little wooden dolls that fit one inside the other, each year inside the next one. That's how being eleven years old is.

You don't feel eleven. Not right away. It takes a few days, weeks even, sometimes even months before you say eleven when they ask you. And you don't feel eleven, not until you're almost twelve. That's the way it is.

Only today I wish I didn't have just eleven years rattling inside me like pennies in a tin Band-Aid box. Today I wish I was one-hundred-and-two instead of eleven because if I was one-hundred-and-two I'd have known what to say when Mrs. Price put the red sweater on my desk. I would've known how to tell her it wasn't mine instead of just sitting there with that look on my face and nothing coming out of my mouth.

"Whose is this?" Mrs. Price says, and she holds the red sweater up in the air for all the class to see. "Whose?" It's been sitting in the coatroom for a month."

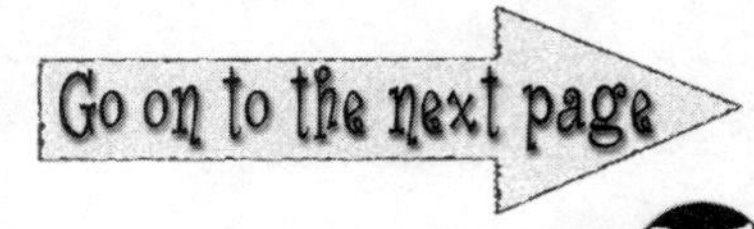

Activity continued

"Not mine," says everybody. "Not me."

"It has to belong to somebody," Mrs. Price keeps saying, but nobody can remember. It's an ugly sweater with red plastic buttons and a collar and sleeves all stretched out like you could use it for a jump rope. It's maybe a thousand years old and even if it belonged to me I wouldn't say so.

Maybe because I'm skinny, maybe because she doesn't like me, that stupid Felice Garcia says, "I think it belongs to Rachel." An ugly sweater like that, all raggedy and old, but Mrs. Price believes her. Mrs. Price takes the sweater and puts it right on my desk, but when I open my mouth nothing comes out.

"That's not, I don't, you're not . . . not mine," I finally say in a little voice that was maybe me when I was four.

"Of course it's yours," Mrs. Price says, "I remember you wearing it once." Because she's older and the teacher, she's right and I'm not.

Not mine, not mine, not mine, but Mrs. Price is already turning to page 32, and math problem number four. I don't know why but all of a sudden I'm feeling sick inside, like the part of me that's three wants to come out of my eyes, only I squeeze them shut tight and bite down on my teeth real hard and try to remember today I am eleven, eleven. Mama is making a cake for me tonight, and when Papa comes home everybody will sing happy birthday, happy birthday to you.

But when the sick feeling goes away and I open my eyes, the red sweater's still sitting there like a big red mountain. I move the red sweater to the corner of my desk with my ruler. I move my pencil and books and eraser as far from it as possible. I even move my chair a little to the right. Not mine, not mine, not mine.

In my head I'm thinking how long till lunch time, how long till I can take the red sweater and throw it over the schoolyard fence, or leave it hanging on a parking meter, or bunch it up into a little ball and toss it in the alley. Except when math period ends Mrs. Price says loud and in front of everybody, "Now, Rachel, that's enough," because she sees I've shoved the red sweater to the tippy-tip corner of my desk and it's hanging all over the edge like a waterfall, but I don't care.

Activity continued

"Rachel," Mrs. Price says. She says it like she's getting mad. "You put that sweater on right now and no more nonsense."

"But it's not . . ."

"Now!" Mrs. Price says.

This is when I wish I wasn't eleven because all the years inside of me—ten, nine, eight, seven, six, five, four, three, two, and one—are pushing at the back of my eyes when I put one arm through one sleeve of the sweater that smells like cottage cheese, and then the other arm through the other and stand there with my arms apart as if the sweater hurts me and it does, all itchy and full of germs that aren't even mine.

That's when everything I've been holding in since this morning, since when Mrs. Price put the sweater on my desk, finally lets go, and all of a sudden I'm crying in front of everybody. I wish I was invisible but I'm not. I'm eleven and it's my birthday today and I'm crying like I'm three in front of everybody. I put my head down on my desk and bury my face in my stupid clown sweater arms. My face all hot and spit coming out of my mouth because I can't stop the little animal noises from coming out of me, until there aren't any more tears left in my eyes, and it's just my body shaking like when you have the hiccups, and my whole head hurts like when you drink milk too fast.

But the worst part is right before the bell rings for lunch. That stupid Phyllis Lopez who is even dumber than Felice Garcia, says she remembers the red sweater is hers! I take it off right away and give it to her, only Mrs. Price pretends like everything's okay.

Today I'm eleven. There's a cake Mama's making for tonight, and when Papa comes home from work we'll eat it. There'll be candles and presents and everybody will sing happy birthday, happy birthday to you, Rachel, only it's too late.

I'm eleven today. I'm eleven, ten, nine, eight, seven, six, five, four, three, two, and one, but I wish I was one-hundred-and-two. I wish I was anything but eleven, because I want today to be far away already, far away like a tiny kite in the sky, so tiny-tiny you have to close your eyes to see it.

Activity continued

1. Rachel doesn't say anything back to Mrs. Price. When Mrs. Price insists that the sweater is Rachel's. What does this tell you about Rachel?

What this tells me about Rachle is that shes Respectfel to grownup

2. What kind of person is the teacher, Mrs. Price? Give an example of something that she says or does to support your answer.

Mrs. Price is a Mad parson Because no Body would tell her Ohs sweater it was

3. Rachel decides to silently push the sweater to the edge of the desk. What does this tell you about her?

It tells me that it was not her Sweter if it wasn't she would have push it over the fence.

Activity continued

4. Rachel becomes very upset and begins to cry. Based on what you know about her, do you think that she is overreacting? Explain.

yes Because it is not all of that

5. At the end of the story, Mrs. Price pretends that everything is okay. What does this reveal about Mrs. Price?

she is a mean parson

1. Which answer BEST describes the picture you form of Mrs. Price from this story?

   A. thoughtful and compassionate

   B. hard-working and disciplined

   C. not sensitive or harsh

   D. humorous

2. All of the following describe Rachel EXCEPT

   A. quiet

   B. sensitive

   C. outspoken

   D. eleven

3. Which of the following is NOT a detail about Rachel from the story?

   A. It is her birthday.

   B. She is the shortest girl in the class.

   C. She is skinny.

   C. She has a large family.

Analyze Setting

Setting

The setting is where and when a story takes place. The setting is directly related to the characters and the events that happen. A story can take place in the past, present, or future, and it can occur any place imaginable. Sometimes an author describes the setting in detail. Other times, you learn about the setting simply from reading the story and finding out where the characters are and what they are doing.

For example, can you picture the setting from the story, *Eleven*, which you just read in the previous lesson? The setting is a school classroom. This is a place you are quite familiar with. The events that happen in the story and the dialogue between Rachel and Mrs. Price depend on this setting.

Or, you might read a story about the adventures of a boy who lives on Mars. The story obviously takes place in the future in a place that only your imagination and the author's description can take you to.

Now, read this story from Indian folklore. As you read, pay attention to the story's setting.

Water from the Well

—retold by Uma Krishnaswami

One summer, in the kingdom of Vijayanagar, the rains were late. No black thunderclouds darkened the sky. A drought so severe hit the land that the crops wilted and died and the temple ponds dried up. The water in all the wells sank lower and lower, and getting it out became harder and harder work.

Now, in that land lived a king, and in that king's court was a minister. His name was Rama, and he came from the village of Tenali. Lest he should be confused with all the other Ramas in the kingdom, everybody called him Tenali Rama.

Tenali Rama's wife had a small garden, with two banana trees she had planted with loving care. She also had a small stand of *tulasi*, holy basil for medicine and prayer. And last

Go on to the next page

but not least, she had a jasmine plant with waxy white blossoms. It filled the night air with fragrance and made her the envy of the neighborhood. So when her beloved plants began to wilt, Tenali Rama's wife said to him, "Go pull up a bucket of water from the well, husband, and water my plants before they die."

Rama went to the well and peered in. The water level was so low he had to crane his neck to see it.

"This is a fine spot, wife, to put your poor husband in," he said, though not so loudly that his wife could hear him. "The well is deep, and I will have to work very hard to draw water from it."

Tenali Rama looked around him for inspiration. Just then, he heard a rustle behind the banana trees. Sneaking a quick glance that way, he spied four men, obviously up to no good at all.

Thieves! said Tenali Rama in the quiet of his own mind. They look like thieves.

He yawned a loud yawn, making sure the four men saw him, then he went inside the house and threw open all the windows. In the loudest voice he could summon, he said, "O my wife, there is a famine in the land, and thieves are everywhere. They might come here too, and rob us. And you with your precious jewels, your gold chain, the diamond earrings you got from your mother!"

"So what shall we do?" said his wife.

"Take all your jewels," shouted Tenali Rama, "put them in a box, and throw it into the well."

"You don't have to shout," said his wife. "What a silly idea." But Tenali Rama had closed the windows quickly, so the thieves did not hear her.

"What a fool!" said the first thief.

"A tired fool is the best kind to rob," said the second.

"Tonight, at nine," said the third.

"Right here, behind the banana trees," said the fourth.

And the thieves tiptoed away, laughing to themselves.

Eight o'clock came. "Did you water my plants?" asked Tenali Rama's wife.

"It will be done," said Rama.

"A promise is a promise," said his wife.

"A promise is a promise," Tenali Rama reassured her.

Then he filled a box with bricks and rocks, dragged it to the well, and dropped it in. He blew out the lamps in all the rooms of his house and whispered to his wife to wait with him in the dark. Now, Tenali Rama's wife was used to her husband behaving oddly on occasion, so she humored him.

Nine o'clock came, and so did the thieves. They gathered behind the banana tree. Carefully, looking all around them as thieves will, they hurried to the well.

"I see it!" said the first thief.

"The box! There it is!" exclaimed the second.

"Quick, empty the well!" said the third. "There's the rope, and here's the bucket."

"What shall we do with the water?" asked the fourth.

"Throw it on the ground," said the other three.

The four thieves set to work. In no time at all, they had watered the banana trees and the jasmine plant. Another few buckets, and there was enough water to save the tulasi plant, whose leaves Tenali Rama's wife steeped in hot water when anyone in the family had a sore throat.

All out of breath, the thieves paused to take a break.

"There's still a lot of water in the well," said the first.

"Maybe we should come back tomorrow," said the second.

"To finish the job," said the third and fourth together.

"So kind of you," said Tenali Rama, coming out of his house with his palms together in greeting. "Actually, you needn't bother. You've watered the garden quite enough for a week, I should think. My wife and I are much obliged to you."

And Tenali Rama smiled, went back inside the house, and closed the door. The four most embarrassed thieves in town left as quickly as they could.

Go on to the next page

Activity

Directions Answer the following questions to analyze the setting of this story.

1. Describe the setting of this story.

The setting is ina well at a king dom

2. The village of Tenali is experiencing a drought. Explain why this setting has an impact on the plot of the story.

Because it has a lot Of water

3. What details about the setting could change without altering the story very much?

Where it is

Activity continued

4. Which aspects of the setting would significantly change the story?

~~If you change the charther~~
If there was not a drate

5. The garden and the well are a central part of the setting.
How do they affect the characters and the events that happen?

Granden need to be water
and it was low

Go on to the next page

1. Which of the following BEST describes the setting of this story?

   A. the king's castle in the kingdom of Vijayanagar

   B. the garden and home of Tenali Rama

   C. a village in southern India

   D. an Iroquois village

2. During what season does this story take place?

   A. summer

   B. fall

   C. spring

   D. winter

3. All of the following are details from the story that describe the setting EXCEPT:

   A. the small garden where Tenali Rama's wife grows banana trees and basil

   B. the deep well where the water sank lower and lower due to the drought

   C. the jail where the thieves will go

   D. the kingdom of Vijayanagar

Analyze Plot

Plot

The chain of events in a story is the plot. Within the plot is always a problem that needs to be solved. The problem or conflict is what keeps readers involved in the story and interested in finding out what will happen next. The conflict builds suspense and tension. When the conflict is resolved, the story draws to a conclusion.

Certain words signal time and the sequence of events. Look for words such as *first, second, third, last, next, after, before, while, later,* and *then* to help you keep track of the order of events.

Follow the plot in the following passage. Notice the words that signal the sequence of events and the problem that arises.

Jamie drew her arm out of the water and *then* looked at the time on her waterproof watch, the watch that her best friend had let her borrow for the weekend. No wonder she was hungry. It was already 1:30. She always lost track of time when she was in the ocean. She wanted to eat lunch, but *first* she would wait for a wave she could ride into shore. The *next* wave came and *then*, in the distance, she saw a giant one approaching. *At the same time* that it approached, a dangerous jellyfish bobbed near her. Terrified of getting stung, Jamie waved her arms frantically and began swimming to the right. *Before* she was ready to take on the huge wave coming toward her, however, it smashed into her and sent her somersaulting. *After* rising to the surface and regaining her balance, she realized that her arm felt strangely different. She peered down to find that the watch was gone.

If you were to finish reading this entire story about Jamie, you would find out if she recovers her friend's watch. Jamie's problem naturally draws you into the plot.

Activity **Directions** Read the story below. Then answer the questions.

Sarah Tops

—by Isaac Asimov

I came out of the Museum of Natural History and was crossing the street on my way to the subway, when I saw the crowd about halfway down the block; and the police cars, too. I could hear the whine of an approaching ambulance.

For a minute I hesitated, but then I walked on. The crowds of the curious just get in the way of officials trying to save lives. My Dad, who's a detective on the force, complains about that all the time, and I wasn't going to add to the difficulty myself.

I just kept my mind on the term paper I was going to have to write on air pollution for my 7th-grade class and mentally arranged the notes I had taken on the Museum program on the subject.

Of course, I knew I would read about it in the afternoon papers. Besides, I would ask Dad about it after dinner. Sometimes he talked about cases without giving too much of the real security details. And Mom and I never talk about what we hear, anyway.

After I asked, Mom looked kind of funny and said, "He was in the museum at the very time."

I said, "I was working on my term paper. I was there first thing in the morning."

Mom looked worried. "There might have been shooting in the museum."

"Well, there wasn't," said Dad soothingly. "This man tried to lose himself in the museum and he didn't succeed."

"I would have," I said. "I know the museum, every inch."

Dad doesn't like me boasting, so he frowned at me. "The thugs who were after him didn't let him get away entirely. They caught up with him outside, knifed him, and got away. We'll catch them, though. We know who they are.

Activity continued

He nodded his head. "They're what's left of the gang that broke into that jewelry store two weeks ago. We managed to get the jewels back, but we didn't grab all the men. And not all the jewels either. One diamond was left. A big one—worth thirty thousand dollars."

"Maybe that's what the killers were after," I said.

"Very likely. The dead man was probably trying to cross the other two and get off with the one stone for himself. They turned out his pockets, practically ripped off his clothes, after they knifed him."

"Did they get the diamond?" I asked.

"How can we tell? The woman who reported the killing came on him when he was just barely able to breathe. She said he said three words to her very slowly. 'Try . . . Sarah . . . Tops.' Then he died."

"Who is Sarah Tops?" asked Mom.

Dad shrugged. "I don't know. I don't even know if that's really what he said. The woman was pretty hysterical. If she's right and that's what he said, then maybe the killers didn't get the diamond. Maybe the dead man left it with Sarah Tops, whoever she is. Maybe he knew he was dying and wanted to give it back and have it off his conscience."

"Is there a Sarah Tops in the phone book, Dad?" I asked.

Dad said, "Did you think we didn't look? No Sarah Tops, either one P or two P's. Nothing in the city directory. Nothing in our files. Nothing in the FBI files."

Mom said, "Maybe it's not a person. Maybe it's a firm. Sarah Tops Cakes or something."

"Could be," said Dad. "There's no Sarah Tops firm, but there are other kinds of Tops and they'll be checked out for anyone working there named Sarah. It'll take days of dull routine."

I got an idea suddenly and bubbled over. "Listen, Dad, maybe it isn't a firm either. Maybe it's a thing. Maybe the woman didn't hear 'Sarah Tops' but Sarah's top; you know a *top* that you spin. If the dead guy has a daughter named Sarah, maybe he gouged a bit out of her top and stashed the diamond inside and . . ."

Activity continued

Dad pointed his finger at me and grinned, "Very good, Larry," he said. "A nice idea. But he doesn't have a daughter named Sarah. Or any relative by that name as far as we know. We've searched where he lived and there's nothing reported there that can be called a top."

"Well," I said, sort of let down and disappointed. "I suppose that's not such a good idea anyway, because why should he say we ought to try it? He either hid it in Sarah's top or he didn't. He would know which. Why should he say we should *try* it?"

And then it hit me. What if . . .

Dad was just getting up, as if he were going to turn on television, and I said, "Dad, can you get into the museum this time of evening?"

"On police business? Sure."

"Dad," I said kind of breathless. "I think we better go look. *Now*. Before the people start coming in again."

"Why?"

"I've go a silly idea. I . . . I . . ."

Dad didn't push me. He likes me to have my own ideas. He thinks maybe I'll be a detective, too, some day. He said, "All right. Let's follow up your lead whatever it is."

He called the museum, then we took a taxi and got there just when the last purple bit of twilight was turning to black. We were let in by a guard.

I'd never been in the museum when it was dark. It looked like a huge, underground cave, with the guard's flashlight seeming to make things even darker and more mysterious.

We took the elevator up to the fourth floor where the big shapes loomed in the bit of light that shone this way and that as the guard moved his flash.

"Do you want me to put on the light in this room?" he asked.

"Yes, please," I said.

There they all were. Some in glass cases; but the big ones in the middle of the large room. Bones and teeth and spines of giants that ruled the earth hundreds of millions of years ago.

Activity continued

"I want to look close at that one," I said. "Is it all right if I climb over the railing?"

"Go ahead," said the guard. He helped me.

I leaned against the platform, looking at the grayish plaster material the skeleton was standing on.

"What's this?" I said. It didn't look much different in color from the plaster on which it was lying.

"Chewing gum," said the guard, frowning. "Those darn kids . . ."

"The guy was trying to get away and he saw his chance to throw this . . . keep it away from them . . ." Before I could finish my sentence Dad took the gum from me. He squeezed it, then pulled it apart. Something inside caught the light and flashed. Dad put it in an envelope. "How did you know?" he asked me.

"Well, look at it," I said.

It was a magnificent skeleton. It had a large skull with bone stretching back over the neck vertebrae. It had two horns over the eyes, and a third one, just a bump, on the snout. The nameplate said *Triceratops*.

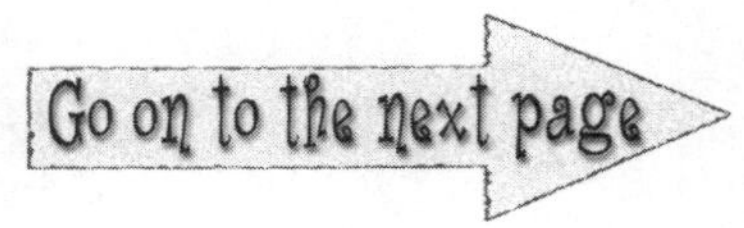
Go on to the next page

Activity continued

1. What happens at the beginning of the story as Larry, the narrator, comes out of the Museum of Natural History?

2. Why doesn't Larry stop to find out what is happening?

3. What is revealed about the case during dinner?

4. During dinner, Larry suddenly has an idea that looks at the problem from a different angle. What is Larry's idea? How is it different?

5. Why do Larry and his father return to the museum?

Activity continued

6. How does Larry solve the mystery?

____

____

7. The plot of the story revolves around a misunderstanding. Explain what this misunderstanding is.

____

____

8. Why is this story's plot exciting?

____

____

9. Larry tells his father that they should return to the museum "now," before the people start coming again. What might Larry have been concerned about?

____

____

10. Towards the end of the story, Dad doesn't make Larry explain his reason for returning to the museum. What effect does this have on the plot?

____

____

1. What were the thugs trying to get from the man who died?

   A. money

   B. a diamond

   C. a case of jewelry

   D. a top

2. How does Larry figure out the solution to the mystery?

   A. He realizes that everyone is misinterpreting the words "try . . . Sarah . . . Tops."

   B. He has a dream and realizes that the solution is in the dinosaur.

   C. He remembers something else that the dying man said.

   D. He finds Sarah Tops in the phone book.

3. All of the following ideas to crack the case are discussed EXCEPT:

   A. There could be a woman named Sarah Tops.

   B. There could be company or firm named Sarah Tops.

   C. There is a restaurant or hotel named Tops.

   D. The name Tops could be spelled with two p's.

Analyze Problem/Solution

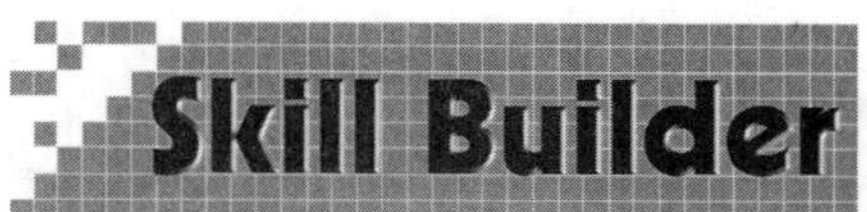

Problem/ Solution

In stories, characters face problems that need solutions. Understanding a character's problems and how he or she goes about solving them will help you follow the plot.

This main problem is established early on in the story and lets you know what the story will be about. As the plot progresses, different problems may arise, although they are usually related to the main problem. Eventually, the events lead to a turning point. This is the point where a major change occurs for a character. The turning point may be a significant crisis or the point where the problem ends and the solution begins.

Think back to the story *Sarah Tops,* which you read in Lesson 7. The problem in this story is that a crime has been committed and Larry's father needs to figure out who Sarah Tops is in order to solve the crime. Throughout the story, Larry tries to find a solution. The intriguing problem draws you into the story and keeps you reading, eager to find out how the crime is solved.

Directions Read the following scene from "The Wonderful Wizard of Oz." After you read the scene, answer the questions that follow.

Characters

DOROTHY
TOTO, her dog
WITCH OF THE NORTH
MUNCHKINS
SCARECROW
TIN WOODMAN
COWARDLY LION
GUARDIAN OF THE GATE
THE WIZARD OF OZ
WICKED WITCH OF THE WEST
GLINDA THE GOOD, Witch of the South
FLORIA, her lady-in-waiting

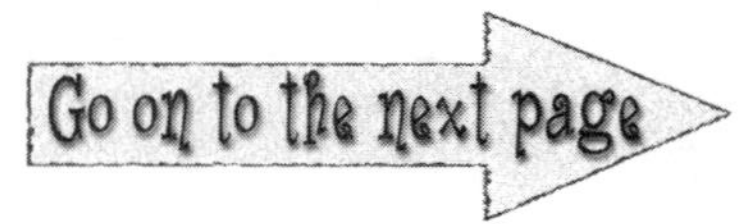

Activity continued

SCENE 1

SETTING: The Country of the Munchkins, in the Land of Oz. Low platform is at center, and at right is fence with pile of straw beside it.

AT RISE: DOROTHY, *with TOTO beside her, sits on platform. Down center is pair of silver slippers.* SCARECROW, *half hidden by straw, is propped up against fence.*

DOROTHY (*Looking around*)**:** TOTO, this place doesn't look familiar to me at all. That cyclone must have carried us far away from home! (*She stands, walks about, confused.*) Toto, I believe we're lost. (WITCH OF THE NORTH *enters right, as several* MUNCHKINS *run left.)*

WITCH OF THE NORTH: Welcome, most noble sorceress, to the Country of the Munchkins in the Land of Oz.

DOROTHY (*Somewhat frightened*)**:** Why, who are you?

WITCH: I am the Witch of the North, a friend of these Munchkins, whose country you are now in. We are all grateful to you for killing the wicked Witch of the East, and wish to serve you in any way possible. *(*MUNCHKINS *make bobbing curtsies.*)

DOROTHY: *You* are very kind, but . . . I didn't kill anyone.

WITCH: You didn't, but your house did. You see, your farmhouse was picked up by the cyclone and landed here in Munchkin, right on top of the wicked Witch of the East, killing her and freeing us from her hateful reign. (*Points to slippers*) See, there are the silver slippers that she wore! She was so old and mean that after she was killed, she just dried up and blew away. Please accept the shoes as a token of our thanks for freeing us from the Witch. 'Tis said they have magic powers, but I know not what they are. (*She sits on platform.*)

DOROTHY: (*Puzzled*) Dear me, what a strange place. Are you a *real* witch? (*She sits beside* WITCH.)

WITCH: Yes, indeed, but I am a good witch, and the people love me.

Activity continued

DOROTHY: But I thought all witches were wicked.

WITCH: Oh, no. That is a great mistake. Of the four witches in the Land of Oz, two of us, who live in the North and South, are good witches, and those in the East and West are wicked witches. Now that the Witch of the East is dead, there is but one wicked witch in all the Land of Oz—the one who lives in the West.

DOROTHY: Perhaps you can tell me how I can get back to Kansas and Aunt Em. She'll be dreadfully worried, you know. And my dog, Toto, always gets upset in a strange place. (TOTO *sits up and barks furiously*. MUNCHKINS *laugh heartily*.)

WITCH: I do not know where Kansas is, Dorothy. But there is one person in Oz who will surely know.

DOROTHY (*With excitement*)**:** Who is he? And where can I find him?

WITCH: Our mighty wizard, the Wizard of Oz—he will tell you how to get back to Kansas. I have never seen him, for he lives in the Emerald City, a wondrously beautiful city whose gates are studded with jewels.

DOROTHY (*Anxiously*)**:** Is he a good man?

WITCH: He is a good *wizard*. Whether he is a man or not, I do not know.

DOROTHY: We'll go right away. How can I get there? (*She rises.*)

WITCH: Follow the yellow brick road through the Great Forest, and that will lead you to the Emerald City. But wear the silver slippers, for they will keep you from harm. One more thing I can do for you. I will give you my magic kiss; no one will dare injure a person who has been kissed by the Witch of the North. (*She rises, kisses* DOROTHY *on forehead.*) And now goodbye. We in Munchkin will always be ready to welcome you back. A safe journey! (WITCH *exits left, followed by* MUNCHKINS, *waving cheerfully.*)

DOROTHY: Come, Toto. (*Puts on slippers*) They fit! (TOTO *jumps up and down excitedly*. DOROTHY *walks a few steps, then notices* SCARECROW.)

Go on to the next page

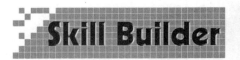

Activity continued

Oh, my gracious, Toto, look—a funny stuffed man. (*Bends over him*) Why, it's a scarecrow. But such a mournful-looking face! (*Brushes straw off him.* SCARECROW *moves slightly, then grins at her.*)

SCARECROW: Good day.

DOROTHY: (*Jumping back in alarm*): Oh! I didn't know you were alive. *(Helping him up*) I never knew scarecrows could be alive.

SCARECROW: *(Testily)*: Of course I'm alive. (*He looks at TOTO curiously.*) But what is that odd little animal? And who are you, and where are you going?

DOROTHY: My name is Dorothy. This is Toto, my dog. We live in Kansas, but a cyclone picked up our house and when the wind died down we found ourselves in Oz. The good Witch of the North told us that the Wizard of Oz in the Emerald City could help us get back to Kansas.

SCARECROW (*Puzzled*)**:** Where is the Emerald City? And who is the Wizard of Oz?

DOROTHY: Why, you don't know?

SCARECROW (*Sadly*)**:** No, indeed. You see, I am only stuffed with straw so I have no brains at all.

DOROTHY: No brains at all?

SCARECROW (*Shaking his head*)**:** None at all. I don't mind my legs, arms, and body being stuffed because I can't get hurt. But with my head stuffed with straw instead of brains, how am I ever to know anything? (*Sadly*) I'm really just a fool.

DOROTHY (*Sympathetically*)**:** You're not a fool! But I understand how you feel. If you come with me, I'll ask the Wizard to help you. Perhaps he will give you some brains.

SCARECROW: Oh, thank you, Dorothy.

DOROTHY: Well, come on. Let's be off! (*They exit right. Curtain*)

Activity continued

1. What is Dorothy's problem?

A cyclone picked up her house and Dorothy and her dog Toto landed in Munchkin land. and she can't get back home.

2. How has Dorothy helped the Munchkins solve one of their problems?

Dorothy's house landed on the wiked witch of the East and killed her freeing the Munchkins from her hated reign.

3. How does Dorothy plan to solve her problem?

Dorothy had planned to go to Emerald City to see the wizard of Oz and ask him how to get back home.

4. What is the Scarecrow's problem?

His problem is that he doesn't have a brain because he's made out of straw.

5. What does Dorothy suggest to the Scarecrow to help him solve his problem?

She tells him to go to Emerald City to ask the wizard of Oz to ask him for a brain.

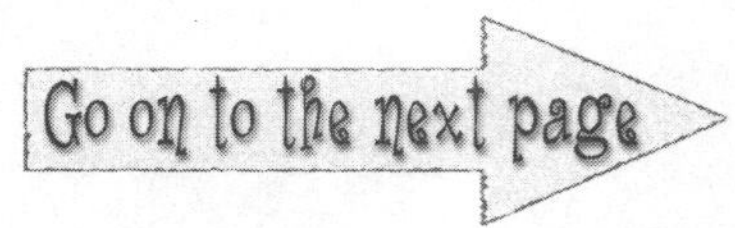

1. What is the cause of Dorothy's problem?

   A. a wicked witch

   B. a cyclone

   C. her dog who ran away

   D. the Wizard of Oz

2. Who does Dorothy need to see to help her get back home?

   A. the Witch of the South

   B. the Witch of the North

   C. the Wizard of Oz

   D. the Scarecrow

3. Which of the following is NOT a reason that the Scarecrow accompanies Dorothy?

   A. He wants to see the Wizard.

   B. He doesn't want to be alone.

   C. He wants to get brains.

   D. He wants help.

Directions: Read the selection and answer the questions.

The Playoffs
By Linda Chiara

"Stri-i-i-ke three!" the umpire shouted.

Dave wiped the sweat off his brow, turned and trudged back to the dugout, leaving a thin line in the dirt as he dragged the bat behind him.

Coach Richards ruffled Dave's silky hair. "Good try," he said. "You just need more batting practice."

I hate it when he's nice like that, thought Dave. He just doesn't want to hurt my feelings. If Coach thought I could hit, he'd yell at me like he does the others: "Dave! Are you asleep? You swing the bat like my GRANDMOTHER!"

That's what hurt most. If Coach had any confidence in him, he'd yell instead of being nice.

Dave's teammates understood how embarrassed he felt. At one time or another, they'd all been humiliated at the plate.

All except Alex.

Alex waited until Dave flopped down on the bench, stabbing the dirt with the toes of his cleats.

"Man, you reek," Alex said under his breath. "That was your third strikeout. Are you single-handedly trying to keep us out of the championships?"

Dave looked down. He didn't want to see the smirk on Alex's face.

"I batted three times too, but at least I didn't blow it! I got on base each time."

As if Dave hadn't noticed. He saw Alex hit a single and two doubles. Whenever Alex walked to the plate, Dave cheered because Coach insisted on good team spirit. But in his mind, he'd chant, *"Strike out…strike out"* like a mantra, feeling guilty with every thought.

The cries of his teammates jolted Dave back to reality. "We won! We won! We're going to the championships!" they said, then chanted, "The Hawks are the best! Better than the rest!"

They hugged and high-fived each other until Coach gathered them for a pep talk.

Go On

Afterward, Coach squeezed Dave's shoulders as he walked him out of hearing range.

"You're a good player, Dave. You swing late, that's all. Practice swinging faster. Watch Alex's stance and how he swings. He rarely strikes out."

Great, thought Dave. *Mr. Perfect is now my role model.* He looked up and saw Alex standing a few feet away, a weird little grin on his face. Dave's stomach tightened and his face grew hot, knowing Alex had listened in on the conversation. Coach didn't notice Alex standing there. That very second Dave wished the earth would swallow him whole. Then he'd never have to look at Alex's perfect teeth or his perfect batting stance or his perfect anything anymore.

Dave knelt down and forced his glove into his backpack. Two books fell out. Alex picked them up. Looking them over, he crowed, "Ohh, lookey here. Baseball books. Let's see, Jackie Robinson's biography and…what's this? *The Rules of Baseball?*"

"Give'em to me, Alex," Dave said through clenched teeth, reaching for the books. Alex laughed and yanked them away.

"You carry around a rule book with you? No wonder you can't hit! You're too busy reading to practice."

Dave's face burned. He knew the guys would think he was a nerd but he loved reading about baseball almost as much as he loved playing it.

"At least I know how to read!" Dave shot back, knowing as soon as the words left his mouth that they sounded dumb.

That night at bedtime, Dave picked up a book from his nightstand. His favorite player suggested swinging the bat 100 times a day to become a better hitter. Dave hopped out of bed, picked up his bat and started swinging. *One…swing…two…swing…three…swing…I can do this…23…swing …24…swing…*his palms started to sweat…*48…swing…*the bat felt heavier…*86…*come on. You can do it. Only 14 more. His shoulder ached. *Ninety-nine…swing…100…swing.* He dropped the bat and fell into bed.

"I'll do this every day," he vowed, rubbing his shoulder. "I'll show Alex."

For the rest of the week, Dave swung his bat constantly.

At practice Coach Richards said, "Good job, Dave. You're swinging faster and your stance is more like Alex's." Still Dave didn't get a hit.

The big day finally arrived. Dave's stomach felt like a butterfly boxing match.

The game was close, right up to the last inning. The other team was ahead 4–3. Dave could barely breathe. He figured the batting order in his head, hoping he wouldn't be the last to bat. If there were two outs when it was his turn, he was sure he'd blow it. *Please*, he pleaded silently, *don't let me bat last.*

There were two outs when Joey Rodriquez stepped up to the plate. Joey slammed a solid line drive that put him on first.

It was Alex's turn.

Dave clenched his fists. *I don't want to be the one who loses the championship, he thought. If Alex strikes out, the pressure will be off me.*

Alex swung and missed. Dave's emotions flip-flopped. His stomach felt like he was on a tilt-a-whirl.

Plunk. The sound of the bat hitting the ball was music to Dave's ears, yet the nauseousness continued. Alex ran to second as Joey scooted to third.

Dave adjusted his batting helmet. Coach leaned down and whispered, "You only need to get to first base to tie the score."

Dave walked to the plate, cradled the bat and rubbed some dirt between his hands. He spotted Alex on second base, looking disgusted. Dave grimaced, wiped his hands on his pants, tapped the side of his right shoe with the bat and got into his stance.

Zoom. The ball went by so fast he didn't have time to react.

"Strike one!" barked the ump.

Dave twisted the bat in his hands. *Zoom*. He swung and missed as the second pitch flew by.

"Strike two!"

"Ah, man…come on!" Alex shouted from second.

Focus, Dave thought. *Just get to base.*

Joey, on third, led off the bag, ready to run on anything. Alex stepped off the base too, but his face showed no confidence, only defeat.

The third pitch left the pitcher's hand. It came hard and fast. Dave swung and missed.

In the second between the ump yelling "strike three" and Alex moaning "nooooo," Dave saw the catcher drop the ball.

This was it! Dave realized.

He dropped the bat and ran like a man afire for first base. Joey, who was already halfway home, kept on running. As Alex shook his head dejectedly and took a step toward the dugout, confusion erupted.

"Run, Alex, run!" shouted Coach Richards.

Go On

Alex didn't understand but did what he was told. The catcher scooped up the ball just as Joey slid home. Instinctively, the catcher threw to first but overshot the plate. Coach Richards jumped up and down like a wild man, waving Alex home.

Alex rounded third and flew home. They'd won! Coach ran into the infield and grabbed Dave by both shoulders, shaking him back and forth like a rag doll.

"How did you know to run on a third strike if the catcher dropped the ball?" Coach roared.

"I guess I read it somewhere," Dave said sheepishly, grinning. His heart felt like it was racing a thousand beats a minute.

Since that day, Dave has heard Alex's version of the championship game a million times. Alex still brags about being the winning run.

Deep down, though, Dave knows that it takes a lot more than a winning run to be a champion.

1. Dave thinks that

A. he is a bad baseball player.

B. he is a good baseball player.

C. he should quit playing baseball.

D. reading about baseball isn't fun.

2. How do you think Dave's teammates feel about Dave?

A. They think he is a good baseball player.

B. They don't feel that they can depend on him.

C. They dislike Dave as a person.

D. They think he is the best player on the team.

3. Which of the following statements BEST expresses the theme of the story?

A. Life is a learning process and you have to work hard to succeed.

B. Baseball is the best sport to play.

C. People can be mean sometimes and you just have to ignore them.

D. People need to learn when to give up.

4. Which choice BEST describes Alex?

A. He is a good friend and teammate.

B. He is fast and clever.

C. He is cruel and insensitive.

D. He is a poor baseball player.

5. One way Dave prepares himself for the championship is by

A. reading a book about baseball rules.

B. watching baseball movies.

C. practicing with Alex everyday.

D. practicing with his father.

How to Write a Short Response

What's Expected on the Test

Your first task on the Ohio Proficiency Test, is to read a selection and answer multiple-choice questions. You practiced doing this in the lessons that you just completed. The second task on the test is to write a short response to a question based on a selection. You will learn how to write a short response now.

Unlike the multiple-choice part of the test where you have answers to choose from, the short-response part of the test requires you to think on your own. In most cases, your short-response answer will be anywhere from one to a few sentences long.

Test-Taking Strategies

Read the Question Carefully

Before you write your answer, make sure that you understand the question and that your response fits the question. Don't include details or information that the question doesn't ask for.

Go Back to the Story

Go back to the story to find the details that you need in order to answer the question. Even if you know the answer to the question, go back to the story and double-check to make sure that you are right.

Answer the Entire Question

Sometimes a question has two parts or asks you to give several examples. Make sure that you answer all parts of the question. If the question asks for one example, only give one example. If the question asks you to support your answer with examples or details from the story, make sure that you give more than one example or detail.

Check for Accuracy

Spell the names of places and characters correctly. If you are summarizing events that happened, make sure that you write about them in the correct order. If you are citing something a character said, make sure that you record the statement accurately.

Use Only the Space Provided

Think about what you want to write and make sure your response fits in the space provided. The space that you are given is a good indication of approximately how long your answer should be.

READING GUIDE

Directions Read the following scene from the *Wizard of Oz* and put your key reading strategies to work. The questions on the right will guide you as you read. Then read the short-response question. Think about the scene from the play and write your response on the lines provided.

Scene 2

1 **SETTING:** *The Yellow Brick Road, in the Great Forest. Path of yellow cloth or paper goes across stage. Down left is pile of logs; backdrop of tree represents forest.*

AT RISE: TIN WOODMAN *stands motionless down left, arm upraised, holding ax over pile of logs.* DOROTHY, TOTO, *and* SCARECROW *enter right.*

DOROTHY (*Noticing* TIN WOODMAN)**:** Oh, look! (*Rushing over to him*) It's a Tin Woodman, but he only half finished his wood chopping. And see–he's been crying!

SCARECROW (*Going to* TINMAN)**:** So he has. (*Studying him*) I've never seen anyone like him before. (WOODMAN *groans*)

WOODMAN (*Haltingly*)**:** Don't stand there staring at me.
2 Help me! Do something! You don't suppose I want to stand here like this, do you?

DOROTHY (*Amazed*)**:** I've never heard of such a thing as a *live* tin woodman! (*To* WOODMAN) What shall we do? How can we help you?

3 **WOODMAN:** Send that straw-stuffed creature to my cottage and bring me my can of oil. I was caught in the rain while chopping wood, and my joints are rusted. Hurry!

SCARECROW: Oh, what a bother!

DOROTHY: Oh, go ahead, Scarecrow. It won't take a minute. (*He exits, grumbling.*)

4 **WOODMAN:** Thank you. What's your name? (TOTO *exits*)

DOROTHY: My name is Dorothy, and this is my dog, Toto. (*She looks about for Toto, calls him.*) Toto! Toto! Oh, well, he'll be back soon. We're from Kansas but got lost in a storm. (*Looking off*) Here comes Scarecrow! (SCARECROW *reenters, holding can of oil. He and*

GUIDED QUESTIONS

1 **Why is the Yellow Brick Road an important part of the setting in relation to the plot?**

2 **What is the Woodman's problem? How do Dorothy and Scarecrow solve it?**

3 **What can you infer about the type of person that the Woodman is based on the way that he refers to the Scarecrow?**

4 **Notice that Toto exits. What is your prediction about where he goes and what will happen to him?**

Go on to the next page

READING GUIDE

DOROTHY *oil* WOODMAN, *who slowly lowers arm and stretches cautiously.*)

WOODMAN (*Smiling*)**:** That's much better. You have no idea how tiresome it is to stand here for two days waiting for someone to save you.

SCARECROW: Dorothy is a kind little girl. She saved me and now she's saved you. Hooray for Dorothy! (*He starts to dance, falls clumsily.* DOROTHY *and* WOODMAN *set* SCARECROW *on his feet, brush him off.*) Thank you. I'm all right now. Let's go Dorothy.

WOODMAN: Where are you going?

DOROTHY: To the Wizard of Oz. He's going to tell me how to get back to Kansas, where I live.

SCARECROW: And he's going to give me some brains.

WOODMAN (*Wistfully*): Do you suppose he would give me a heart? The tinsmith forgot to give me one when he made me, and I would like to be able to have feelings.

DOROTHY: Well—I don't know, but if he can give Scarecrow some brains, he can surely give you a heart.Why
5 don't you come with us?

WOODMAN: I believe I will. (*Sound of lion roaring is heard off in the distance.*)

6 **DOROTHY:** What's that? (TOTO *runs in pursued by* COWARDLY LION, *and hides behind* DOROTHY, *who smacks* LION *on the nose.* LION *sits on his haunches, howling and rubbing nose.*) What do you mean, chasing a little dog that's so much smaller than you? You ought to be ashamed of yourself.

LION: I can't help it. I'm afraid to chase anyone as big as I am.

7 **SCARECROW:** Who ever heard of a cowardly lion?

WOODMAN (*Scornfully*)**:** And you're supposed to be the King of the Beasts!

LION (*Weeping*)**:** I know, but I've always been afraid to fight, and now no one respects me. What can I do?

DOROTHY: I know! Why not come with us to the Wizard of Oz, and see if he can give you some courage!

LION: Do you think he can? Really?

GUIDED QUESTIONS

5 **Based on your own knowledge of human behavior, why do you think that Dorothy is so sure that the Wizard can help everyone?**

6 **Was your prediction about Toto correct? Confirm or revise it.**

7 **How does the Lion act differently than you would expect a lion to act?**

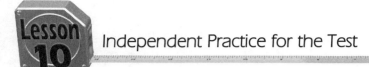

READING GUIDE

DOROTHY: I'm sure he'll try! I want to go back to Kansas. The Scarecrow wants some brains, and the Tin Woodman wants a heart, so you might as well come with us and get some courage.

LION: I might as well. At least it won't be any worse than staying in the forest and being laughed at for being so cowardly.

8 **SCARECROW:** Good! That's settled. Let's go! (*They exit*
9 *right. Curtain*)

10 **1.** What do the characters in this scene have in common? Explain with details from the play.

____

____

____

____

____

GUIDED QUESTIONS

8 **Connect the Scarecrow's actions to his self-image of being a fool. Do you think that he acts like a fool? Explain.**

9 **Set a purpose for reading on. Why would you want to continue reading this play? What do you hope to find out?**

10 **Notice the words *in common*. These words tell you to look for similarities. Use details from the play to show how the characters are similar.**

Activity

Directions Write your answer to the short-response question on the lines provided above.

Self Evaluation

Ask yourself:

- Are the details in my response accurate and relevant to the question?
- Does my response address the question?
- Have I completely answered the question in a clear way?
- Does my response demonstrate a thorough understanding of the story?

How Your Response Will Be Evaluated

Your answer to the short-response question will be evaluated based on a rubric. The rubric lists criteria that a response should have. Teachers use the rubric to evaluate your response. The best score you can receive is a 2. A score of 1 is for a response that meets some of the criteria, while a score of 0 is for a response that does not meet any of the criteria.

Short-Answer Rubric

Score	Criteria
2	• Is complete and appropriate • Demonstrates a thorough understanding of the reading selection • Indicates logical reasoning and conclusions • Is accurate, relevant, comprehensive, and detailed
1	• Is partially appropriate • Contains minor flaws in reasoning or neglects to address some aspect of the item or question • Is mostly accurate and relevant but lacks comprehensiveness • Demonstrates an incomplete understanding of the reading selection or inability to make coherent meaning from the text
0	• Indicates no understanding of the reading selection or item

How Your Response Will Be Evaluated

Question

What do the characters in the scene have in common? Explain with details from the play.

Sample Response

The characters all need something that they don't have. Dorothy wants to find a way home, the Scarecrow wants brains, the Woodman wants a heart, and the Lion wants courage.

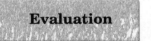

Evaluation

This response would receive a score of 2. It states what the characters have in common and it includes accurate details from the play. The response is also clear and easy to read.

Activity

Directions Look again at your own answer. Use the rubric to evaluate it. Write an evaluation of your response on the lines below.

____

____

____

____

____

Analyze Point of View

Point of View

The point of view is the angle from which a story is told. Who is telling the story affects what is revealed about the characters and the events.

POINT OF VIEW	DEFINITION	EXAMPLE
first-person	One of the characters in the story tells the story. First-person pronouns such as *I*, *me*, *we*, and *our* are used to identify the narrator.	*I* ran outside, with *my* heart fluttering, when *I* heard the noise. *My* neighbors ran out too and *we* all stared at the small plane which had landed near *our* homes. I couldn't believe what I was seeing.
third-person	Someone outside of the story relates the story. Third-person pronouns such as *he*, *she*, *they*, and *them* are used to identify all of the characters.	The people on the block ran outside as soon as *they* heard the noise. *They* all stared in disbelief at the small plane which had landed near *their* homes.
omniscient	An all-knowing narrator relates the story. An *omniscient* point of view allows the narrator to relate the feelings and thoughts of every character. All characters are identified by the pronouns *he*, *she*, *they*, and *them*.	Tim ran out of his house and stared in disbelief at the plane. It looked just like his uncle's plane but he couldn't imagine that his uncle would land here, right near their home. Jared, who lived next door, couldn't believe what he was seeing either. All he kept thinking was *no one is going to believe this*.

Activity

Directions Identify the point of view in each of the passages below.

1. Jeremy sat in his seat and looked around the classroom. Everyone was busy copying notes off the blackboard. Every now and then they would look at him, for a few seconds longer than normal. He was, after all, the new kid in town. People were likely to be curious about him. Although Jeremy naturally began to wonder why everyone was staring at him, he never dreamed that it was his sunglasses. Mr. Kinney didn't allow anyone to wear sunglasses in class. The whole class, except for Jeremy that is, waited anxiously to see what Mr. Kinney was going to do about it.

   This passage is written in Omniscient point of view.

2. I sat in the seat that Mr. Kinney assigned me and looked around the classroom. It was an awful feeling being new and all. I just wished I was back home, in my old town, in my old school with my old friends. At least the kids in my old school wouldn't stare at me like this. Did my clothes not match? Did I look funny? I couldn't help but wonder why everyone kept looking at me. Didn't anyone ever tell them it's not polite to stare, especially at someone who feels so out of place to begin with?

   This passage is written in first - person point of view.

3. Jeremy wished he could just sink into the floor. He didn't think these kids wanted to pick on him or be mean but he couldn't fathom why they kept looking at him. He wondered if they played a joke like this on every new kid. As Mr. Kinney wrote the notes on the blackboard for the students to copy, he tried to think of a way to get Jeremy to take off his sunglasses. The last thing he would want to do to a new student would be to embarrass him. Mr. Kinney knew that the whole class was waiting, however, to see how he would handle this one. No sunglasses was one rule he always enforced. He despised talking to people when he couldn't see their eyes.

   This passage is written in third preson point of view.

Go on to the next page

Activity continued

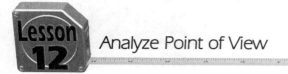

4. I tried really hard not to stare at Jeremy like everyone else was doing. I wanted to scream, ***"Stop staring. You know how terrible you're making him feel?"*** But I didn't say anything of course. If I was a few seats closer to him I would have told him myself that he should take off his sunglasses. Instead, I just waited to see how Mr. Kinney, the strictest teacher in the school, was going to handle it. I prayed that he wouldn't be mean and embarrass this new kid. If only Jeremy knew Mr. Kinney's crazy sunglasses rule.

This passage is written in first - preson point of view.

5. Finally, Mr. Kinney turned around from the blackboard. Everyone's eyes kept switching from him to Jeremy.

"Who can fill our new student, Jeremy, in on some of our class rules?" Mr. Kinney asked.

Miranda raised her hand.

"Go ahead, Miranda," Mr. Kinney said flatly.

"One rule in Mr. Kinney's class is that you can't speak without raising your hand. Another rule is one that you're breaking right now."

"I didn't ask for the commentary, Miranda," said Mr. Kinney. "Please just state the rules for Jeremy."

Jeremy sat with his mouth open trying to figure out what rule he was already breaking after being in class for only seven minutes.

"It's your glasses, Jeremy," continued Miranda with an apologetic look on herface. "Students can't wear sunglasses in class."

Jeremy raised his hand and Mr. Kinney nodded at him. At least now he knew why everyone was looking at him so strangely.

"Sir," said Jeremy. "I really have no choice today. My regular glasses got lost in the move and these prescription sunglasses are all I have until I get new ones."

No one quite expected this answer from Jeremy. Every student couldn't wait to find out how their teacher would handle this one.

"Well, Jeremy," said Mr. Kinney surprising them all, "I guess there's a time for all rules to be broken."

This passage is written in omniscient point of view.

1. What is point of view?
   A. the scenery of a play
   B. the angle that the camera uses to film the story
   C. the angle from which the story is told
   D. the pronoun *I*.

2. If a story is written in first-person point of view, who tells the story?
   A. an outside narrator
   B. a character in the story
   C. an all-knowing narrator
   D. a first child

3. Which point of view lets you know the most about all of the characters?
   A. first-person
   B. third-person
   C. third-person omniscient
   D. none of the above

4. How does changing the point of view in a story affect the story? Explain your answer.

It affect the story about is revild

Lesson 13 Analyze Theme

Theme

The theme is the story's overall message or insight into life that the author wants you to understand. The message is often an important lesson about life. To find the theme in a story, try thinking about the lesson that the characters learn or the lesson that you learned.

The author may state the theme directly or simply hint at it. Either way, you, as the reader, can sum up the theme in a phrase or in a sentence. For example, a story about how kids who pull together during a crisis in their town might have a theme such as: *everyone can make a difference* or *working together gets results*.

Activity

Directions Read *Poogweese* and answer the questions.

Poogweese

A Northwest Coast Indian folktale

—retold by Chief Lelooska

The people of the village were fearful. Fishing had been poor for a long time, and their stores of dried fish were almost gone. Winter would soon be upon them, and they might starve. Every day the village fishermen went out to sea and let down their nets. They fished and fished but caught nothing. The sea seemed without life.

One day the fishermen took their canoes off Bird Island. They let their nets sink deeper and deeper into the cold waters. Then they waited. After awhile there was a strong tugging at the lines. The fishermen knew something very large must be in the net.

It took all hands to pull the heavy net up and heave it into the canoe. Tangled in the net was a strange being like nothing the fishermen had ever seen before! It was clothed in seaweed and appeared to be something like a man. It had huge front teeth and long scraggly hair.

The creature lay there making a squeaking noise. Finally it spoke. "You do not know me, so I will tell you. I am Poogweese, the Merman. I am part man and part fish. I dwell in the world beneath the sea. I am chief messenger of Goomaquay, the lord who controls all the wealth of the ocean. I am his trusted messenger. With the help of the gulls and the loons and the sawbilled ducks, I carry the will of Goomaquay throughout his undersea domain."

Activity continued

The astonished fishermen listened and stared at the strange creature. They did not know what to do. They were afraid if they let Poogweese go he would tell Goomaquay about his captors. This mighty ruler of the sea might get angry and send many great storms. The fishermen would never have any luck fishing again.

"I know what you are thinking," said Poogweese. "You are thinking that if you let me go I will tell Lord Goomaquay. I can understand how you might well be afraid of me, and you certainly should be afraid of my master, but let us strike a bargain."

Then Poogweese explained that if the fishermen would release him to his ocean home he would talk to his master about the fishermen's kindness and about the poor fishing they had endured.

"When Lord Goomaquay realizes that you have freed me and that you know of his existence perhaps life will be better for you," said Poogweese. "And for my thanks I will give you my mask and my song as a gift."

The fishermen looked at one another. They knew they had no choice but to send this powerful creature back to the deep. So they accepted his offer. They could only hope their goodwill would please Lord Goomaquay and that he would improve the fishing and protect them from the great storms.

So the fishermen freed Poogweese from the net. He flopped over the side of the canoe and disappeared into the water. The fishermen looked at one another. One of them said, "He didn't leave us his mask or his song. Maybe he tricked us! Maybe he lied!" Another fisherman cried, "No, the supernatural ones do not lie." Suddenly a shower of bubbles rose from the sea, and the mask of Poogweese floated to the surface.

The fishermen pulled the mask from the water and held it. Then they heard a faint sound. It was weak at first, but they listened and listened, and soon the song of Poogweese filled their ears.

The song described the great house made of copper on the floor of the sea just off Bird Island. This was the home of Lord Goomaquay and all of his retinue of sea monsters and great creatures from the depths.

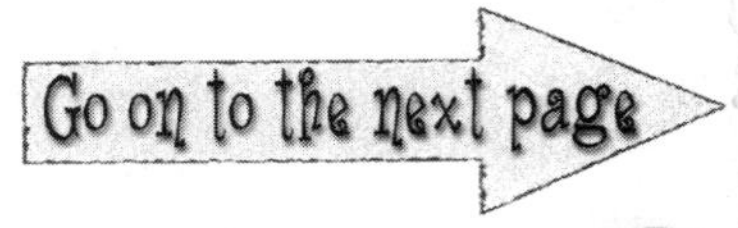

Activity continued

The fishermen were pleased. The weather was fair and the tides were right. They cast out their nets and caught many fish. Then the fishermen carefully wrapped the mask and took it home. They kept it hidden until the next great potlatch of their people. There they showed the mask proudly and described how it had come to them as a gift from Poogweese and Goomaquay, the Lord of the Undersea.

For all time the people would cherish the mask of Poogweese, for it reminded them of their ancestors' adventure in the beginning of time when men and supernatural spirits talked together. It reminded them why their fishermen were successful and safe upon the sea and why their village was wealthy. Through this fateful encounter with Poogweese, the Merman, the people would feel kin to all the beings within the sea forever.

1. What is Poogweese?

____

____

____

2. Name two big ideas that you gain from this tale.

____

____

____

3. What lesson did the fishermen learn about the undersea world?

____

____

____

4. Write a statement explaining the theme of this story.

____

____

____

1. The theme of a story
   - A. tells where the story takes place.
   - B. relates what happens in the story.
   - C. conveys the author's message about life.
   - D. describes the characters.

2. Which choice below *best* describes a theme of *Poogweese*?
   - A. Goodwill and trust pay off.
   - B. Beware of powerful things.
   - C. Life is full of difficulties.
   - D. There are strange creatures living in the sea.

3. Which of the following is NOT a lesson you learn from *Poogweese*?
   - A. Fear a mighty ruler, especially if he or she is evil.
   - B. Show kindness to all creatures.
   - C. Have faith and trust in the word of others.
   - D. none of the above

4. Why are folk tales such as *Poogweese* handed down from generation to generation?

____

____

____

Summarize

Summarizing

When you summarize a story, you give a brief description of the main events or the most important information. To write a summary, you need to first identify what the passage or story is about. Then you can restate the main ideas or events in your own words. When you write a summary, you should exclude unimportant details.

Read this summary of the second scene of *The Wizard of Oz*.

> Dorothy and the Scarecrow continue on the Yellow Brick Road and come upon a rusted Woodman who can't move. They oil him and explain how they are going to see the Wizard of Oz. Dorothy suggests that the Woodman come along with them since he wants a heart. When Dorothy notices that the Lion is chasing Toto, she chastises the Lion. The Lion admits that he is chasing the little dog since he has no courage to fight anyone his own size. Dorothy, once again, suggests that the Lion join them and ask the Wizard for courage.

Notice that this summary only includes the main events that happened. It leaves out details such as *how Dorothy and the Scarecrow stare at the Woodman in amazement* and *Dorothy's explanation to the Woodman about how she got lost*. When you write a summary, ask yourself, *Would I understand the main idea without these details?* If the answer is *no*, then include these details as a part of the summary.

Directions The story below is divided into sections. After you read each section of the story, summarize it on the lines provided.

The Golden Apples

One day, Odin and Loki were returning to Asgard from a trip over the mountains. Since they were having trouble finding food, they were thrilled when they finally came upon a herd of oxen in the valley. Immediately they killed an ox and prepared a fire to cook it.

But a strange thing happened. As the gods roasted the ox over the fire, they discovered that no matter how long they cooked it, it remained raw.

"What does this mean?" said Odin.

"It means I have prevented your fire from cooking the ox," said a deep voice.

The voice seemed to be coming from an enormous eagle sitting in a nearby tree. Actually, the eagle was the giant Thiazi in disguise.

"If you let me eat my fill," said the eagle, "I will make the fire cook your ox."

The gods were so hungry that they quickly agreed. And the eagle coasted down to the ground, then made the fire burn the ox. When the ox was cooked, Thiazi began to eat. He ate and ate and ate.

1. Write a summary of what has happened so far.

____

____

____

____

____

____

Go on to the next page

Activity continued

Angered by such greediness, Loki snatched a long, sharp stick and stabbed the eagle. Loki's weapon stuck into the bird's back, and as the eagle flew up from the ground, he carried Loki away.

The eagle dragged Loki over rock heaps and trees. Afraid his arms might be ripped from his body, Loki begged for help.

"I'll free you only under one condition," said the eagle.

"Anything!" cried Loki.

"You must lure Idun out of Asgard with her basket of apples."

"I can't do that!" said Loki. The goddess Idun guarded the golden apples of youth. Whenever the gods and goddesses started to grow old, they took a bite of Idun's apples and were instantly made young again.

"Do as I say—or you will die!" said Thiazi.

Loki did not want to die, so he agreed to help Thiazi if Thiazi would first release him.

The eagle released him, and Loki tumbled to earth.

2. Write a summary of this section of the story.

____

____

____

____

____

____

Soon after the gods returned home, Loki went to Idun. "I've found some wonderful apples in the forest," he said.

"Indeed?" said she.

Activity continued

"Yes, bring your apples and we'll compare them. If those apples are better than yours, we'll pick them and carry them home."

Idun agreed to do as the trickster said, and she carried her basket of apples into the forest.

Idun and Loki had not traveled far when Thiazi suddenly swooped down in his eagle disguise. The giant snatched Idun and her apples. Then he carried them back to Thrymheim, his hall in the land of the giants.

The gods were horrified when Idun failed to return home that night. Since her golden apples of youth were no longer in Asgard, the gods all began to wither and wrinkle with age.

3. Summarize this section of the story.

____

____

____

____

____

____

In a panic, they met in their council.

"When did you last see Idun?" each asked the other.

"I saw her walking into the woods with Loki," said one.

"Seize the scoundrel!" said Odin.

When Loki was brought before the council, he shook with fear.

"You will be put to a slow tortuous death, Loki, if you do not tell us what happened to Idun," said Odin.

Activity continued

"She's imprisoned in Thrymheim," said Loki, trembling, "but I promise I'll save her."

"You must save her at once, or we'll all die soon of old age!" cried a god.

"Lend me your falcon suit, Freya," said Loki, "so I can fly to Jotunheim as quickly as possible."

The goddess Freya handed over her feather suit, and Loki put it on and flew to the land of the giants.

When Loki arrived at Thrymheim, the home of Thiazi, he found Idun there alone. Thiazi was out at sea.

As soon as Loki saw Idun, he cast a spell over her and changed her into a nut. He then clutched the nut with his talons and started back to Asgard.

4. Write a summary of the events that just happened.

____

____

____

____

____

____

When Thiazi returned home and found Idun missing, he became enraged. He donned his plumage and flew after Loki. Thiazi's wings made a terrible rushing sound as he soared through the air to Asgard.

When the gods and goddesses heard the sound of Thiazi's wings, they looked up at the sky and saw an eagle chasing a falcon. They knew at once the eagle was Thiazi and the falcon, Loki; and they quickly built a woodpile.

As soon as Loki passed beyond the walls to Asgard, the gods set fire to their wood.

Activity continued

Flames roared skyward, but Thiazi was flying so swiftly he couldn't stop himself in time, and he sailed directly into the fire.

His bright feathers in flames, Thiazi fell to the ground. When he landed within the walls of Asgard, Odin killed him.

Loki pulled off his falcon costume. He said a spell over the enchanted nut, and it instantly changed back into Idun.

The guardian of the magic apples was saved—and so was the eternal youth of the gods and goddesses.

5. Write a summary of the conclusion of the story.

____

____

____

____

____

____

Go on to the next page

1. If you were to write a summary of the beginning of this story, which would be the most important detail to include in the summary?

   A. The eagle was sitting in a tree.

   B. The eagle was the giant Thiazi in disguise.

   C. The eagle flew down to the ground.

   D. Odin and Loki were together.

2. Which of the following details should NOT be included in a summary of the last section of the story?

   A. Thiazi's wings made a rushing sound as he flew.

   B. The gods and goddesses built a woodpile to trap Thiazi.

   C. Loki changed the nut back into Idun.

   D. The gods are prevented from cooking the ox.

3. Which of the following statements BEST summarizes this story?

   A. Loki used his magic to cast a spell.

   B. The gods and goddesses need the magic apples.

   C. Loki saves Idun, the guardian of the magic apples, from Thiazi.

   D. Odin and Loki were hungry.

4. What are two difficult predicaments that Loki finds himself in? Explain your answer by referring to events in the story.

   ____

   ____

   ____

   ____

Make Inferences

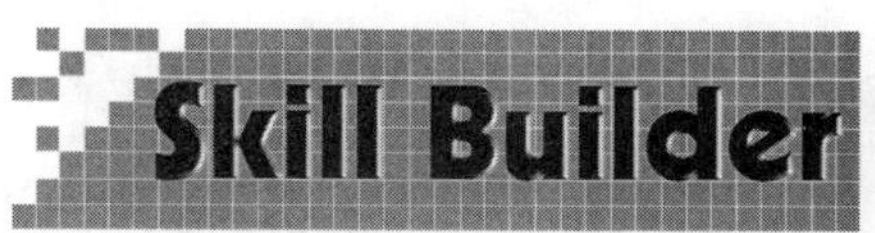

Inferences

An inference is an educated guess. When you make inferences, you use clues in the story to "read between the lines." In other words, you figure out what is going on by filling in information that the author doesn't directly tell you.

For example, imagine that you go to a park to meet some friends and you see them searching for something in the grass. You can **infer** from their actions that someone probably lost something. Although no one told you what is happening, you can figure out what is going on.

As you read, observe what characters do and say. These are clues from the story. Then use your prior knowledge and your own experiences to make inferences or educated guesses about their behavior.

Activity

Directions Read these passages from The *Golden Apples*. Make inferences using the information from the story.

Angered by such greediness, Loki snatched a long, sharp stick and stabbed the eagle. Loki's weapon stuck into the bird's back, and as the eagle flew up from the ground, he carried Loki away.

1. What can you infer about why Loki was carried away?

____

____

Activity continued

"I'll free you only under one condition," said the eagle.

"Anything!" cried Loki.

"You must lure Idun out of Asgard with her basket of apples."

"I can't do that!" said Loki. The goddess Idun guarded the golden apples of youth.

2. What can you infer about Idun's willingness to leave Asgard?

____

____

3. Make an inference about how Loki feels during this conversation.

____

____

In a panic, they met in their council.

"When did you last see Idun?" each asked the other.

"I saw her walking into the woods with Loki," said one.

"Seize the scoundrel!" said Odin.

When Loki was brought before the council, he shook with fear.

4. What can you infer about how Loki is feeling and his predicament?

____

____

Activity continued

As soon as Loki saw Idun, he cast a spell over her and changed her into a nut. He then clutched the nut with his talons and started back to Asgard.

5. Why did Loki change Idun into a nut?

____

____

Go on to the next page

1. Based on the story, what inference can you make about why the golden apples of youth need to be guarded?

   A. Someone might want to steal them.

   B. The apples need to be guarded so that they don't rot.

   C. Someone will eat the apples if they are not watched carefully.

   D. The apples are rotten.

2. Idun agrees to Loki's plan and goes to the forest to compare apples. What can you infer about Idun from this?

   A. She is greedy.

   B. She is silly.

   C. She is courageous.

   D. She is proud of her apples.

3. When Loki was angry at Thiazi's greediness, he stabbed him. What can you infer about Loki?

   A. Loki is clever because he did something to startle Thiazi.

   B. Loki has a temper and can act violently.

   C. Loki is always fighting with others.

   D. Loki has a generous nature.

4. Why do you think that Thiazi wanted Idun and her basket of apples?

   ____

   ____

   ____

   ____

Vocabulary Development

Homophones

Homophones are words that sound alike but are spelled differently and have different meanings. Here is an example of a pair of homophones:

council (*noun*) a group of people who are chosen to oversee the interests of an organization or town

counsel (*verb*) to listen to people's problems and give advice; (*noun*) advice

Other examples of homophones include:

- blue and blew
- plane and plain
- way and weigh

Activity

A. **Directions** Write creative sentences using each pair of homophones.

1. pear-pair ______________________________

____

2. hole-whole ______________________________

____

3. ball-bawl ______________________________

____

4. I'll-aisle ______________________________

____

5. road-rode ______________________________

____

6. one-won ______________________________

____

Go on to the next page

Activity continued

7. heard-herd ____________________

____

8. which-witch ____________________

____

9. week-weak ____________________

____

10. threw-through ____________________

____

B. **Directions** Match each homophone with its definition. Write the letter of the matching definition on the line.

________	**1.** tide	**a.** frog
________	**2.** whether	**b.** fixed in place; not moving
________	**3.** towed	**c.** bound
________	**4.** tied	**d.** if
________	**5.** weather	**e.** flaming signal
________	**6.** stationery	**f.** ebb and flow
________	**7.** toad	**g.** paper
________	**8.** flair	**h.** talent
________	**9.** stationary	**i.** climate
________	**10.** flare	**j.** pulled

1. Homophones are words that
   - A. sound different but mean the same thing.
   - B. sound alike and have identical meanings and have different spellings.
   - C. sound alike but have different meanings and different spellings.
   - D. sound different and have different meanings.

2. Which sentence contains a pair of homophones?
   - A. The dog began to bark as it scraped the bark off the tree.
   - B. I ate at least eight pickles during dinner.
   - C. You might lose your key since this knot that holds it is so loose.
   - D. Michael will read the book that I read.

3. Which choice below is not a pair of homophones?
   - A. ant—aunt
   - B. be—bee
   - C. quiet—quite
   - D. sea—see

4. Why wouldn't a "spell-check" on a computer be able to identify a mistake that you make with homophones?

____

____

____

____

Directions: Read the selection and answer the questions.

The Potter and the Washerman
By Pam Hopper

Once there was a potter who made his living creating beautiful pottery from fine porcelain. Not far from the potter lived a washerman who earned his living making laundry as bright and clean as new.

Both did well in their trades. However, the potter became jealous because he worried that the washerman was more successful than he was. He decided on a secret plan to ruin him.

The potter traveled to the palace and was granted an audience with the king. "What do you wish, potter?" asked the king.

"I have a simple request, Your Majesty," replied the potter. "My neighbor, the washerman, is very good at what he does. I would like to help my neighbor improve his business."

The king stroked his beard. "Why should the washerman's business be of any concern to you?" he asked.

The potter cleared his throat nervously and said, "Well, he is my neighbor, so naturally I desire what is best for him."

The king looked intently at the potter. "What did you have in mind, potter?"

"A challenge, Your Highness. I propose that my neighbor wash one of Your Majesty's esteemed elephants until it is spotlessly clean. To successfully complete a challenge like that would increase his business a hundredfold, I am certain."

Having revealed his plan, the potter's heart hammered so loudly he thought all would hear it. He hoped no one would guess the secret part of his plan: that the washerman's failure to complete such a challenge would ruin his business forever.

"I will consider your request," said the king.

A few days later the potter was summoned before the king.

"I have just spoken with the washerman," the king said, "and he is surprised by your concern for his well-being. He is also troubled by one difficulty with your idea, but knowing you are an accomplished potter, he thought you would be able to help him."

Help the washerman ruin himself? This was better than the potter had anticipated. "I am flattered by the washerman's request, Your Majesty."

"As you know," continued the king, "in order to clean the soiled article, the washerman puts it into a large porcelain basin with water and soap. The concern of the washerman is finding a porcelain basin large enough to wash an elephant. But then he remembered your exceptional talents as a potter, and he suggested that you create such a container."

This was terrible. Create a porcelain basin large enough for an elephant? Impossible. And yet, to refuse could destroy his own reputation. With trembling knees, the potter agreed.

After many weeks of work the elephant-sized porcelain bowl was finally ready. On the day of the challenge the king's largest elephant was brought to the courtyard. The basin was carefully unloaded from the wagon and filled with water and soap.

The washerman stood ready with his best scrub brushes. The elephant was led up the ramp. Trumpeting, it stepped slowly into the delicate basin.

Would the basin hold the elephant?

It would not!

With a crack, the porcelain basin shattered into a thousand pieces, sending a foamy river from the palace courtyard into the town below.

All the people in the courtyard held their breath. What would the king say?

The king smiled gently at the potter. "My elephant is waiting to be bathed, and the washerman waits to prove his ability to wash him spotlessly clean. Would you care to go home and create another basin so the washerman can do this?

The potter gave great thought to his options and he decided he had only one choice: he quickly left the palace courtyard and was never seen again.

As for the washerman, his wisdom so impressed the king that he became one of the most trusted advisers in the royal court.

1. Who tells this story?

A. the washerman

B. the potter

C. an outside narrator

D. the king

2. What is the setting of the story?

A. a large, modern city

B. a small village

C. a royal kingdom

D. a farm

3. Why does the potter choose an elephant for the washerman to clean?

A. He knows that the washerman hates animals.

B. The elephant is very big, so he thinks the washerman will fail.

C. He wants to see if he can build a basin big enough for it.

D. He knows that the king is proud of his elephant.

4. Why do you think the potter runs away and is never seen again?

A. He runs home because he is embarrassed

B. His plan backfires so he runs away thinking the king will put him in jail if he stays.

C. He was angry at the king for making him build the basin.

D. He knows he will not be able to create the basin.

5. What lesson do you think the author is trying to teach?

A. Sometimes people outsmart themselves.

B. People should always be kind to their neighbors.

C. You should be happy with the life that you have.

D. Kings are very wise.

6. Summarize the story.

The Story was about a washerman have to wash an elephant and

Lesson 18 How to Write an Extended Response

What's Expected on the Test?

The third type of question that you will answer on the Ohio Proficiency Test is the extended-response question. Like the short-response question, this type of question requires you to give a written response and to clearly express yourself.

How long is the extended response? Although there is no specific length required, it should thoroughly answer the question. As you can tell by its name, you will be writing an *extended* answer. Your answer will need to contain more information and more details than an answer to a short-response question.

The extended-response question may ask you to analyze a character's personality or to imagine yourself as a character and describe how you would feel in a particular situation. You might have to compare and contrast elements in a story or be asked to write a personal response by interpreting what you have read and connecting it to your own life.

No matter what the extended-response question is, keep in mind the following test-taking strategies.

Jaylan

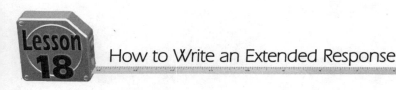

Test-Taking Strategies

Address the Question

Read the question carefully and write an answer that addresses it. In other words, fully answer the question being asked. If the question has two parts, make sure that you answer both parts. For example, a question may ask you to retell what happened at a specific point in a story and to evaluate whether or not a character did the right thing.

Plan and Organize

Before you begin writing, plan in your head, or in a brief outline, what you want to say. Organize your thoughts so that you present your points and examples in the best possible order.

Offer Solid Support

You will always need to support your answer with relevant details from the story. You will use these details to back up and prove the points you make. The examples and details that you choose will demonstrate your understanding of the story and the question.

Include Only Relevant Information

A solid answer sticks to the topic. Don't be tempted to include ideas that have nothing to do with the question. For instance, if the question asks you about the author's purpose, don't add information about the setting just to prove that you read the story.

Read Over Your Answer

Try to leave yourself time to read over your answer. You may have left out a word or something you wrote may be unclear. Slip in transitional words such as *first*, *since*, *therefore*, and *nevertheless* which will make your writing smoother and help you connect your ideas. Correct any mistakes in spelling and punctuation.

READING GUIDE

Directions Put your reading strategies to work as you read the following story. The questions on the right will help you notice and think about important aspects of the story. Then read the extended-response question. Think about the question and the story and write your answer.

Brothers on Ice

—by Donna Gamache

"My brother's one of the referees today," I told my
1 friend Tony as we laced up for the hockey game.

"You mean Mike?" he asked.

I nodded. "Shouldn't hurt our team any."

"You mean he'll go easy on us?"

"Maybe. He didn't say that. I'm just thinking it."

To tell the truth, Mike had actually sort of said the opposite.

"Don't count on special treatment from me, Derek," he'd said as he left for the rink to work an earlier game.

2 "Sure," I said, but I didn't really believe that. After all, what are brothers for? I couldn't see him being hard on us, especially when we were playing the league-leading Redhawks.

"We'll need all the help we can get," Tony said as we headed out for the warmup. "I saw the Redhawks play last weekend. They're big!"

I saw right away what Tony meant. For twelve-year-olds, our team—the Grantly Gophers—is pretty small, except for Tony. That's why we sometimes call him "Tiny T"; and that's why we depend on him a lot on defense. The Redhawks had about five guys as big as Tony. I just hoped they weren't fast.

Mike and the other referee were at one end of the rink,
3 checking the mesh on the net. "Hi, Mike," said, skating past them, but he pretended not to hear. I knew he didn't like the idea of referring his own brother, but when you live in a small town, that sometimes happens.

"They'll try to pair me with an adult for the first year," Mike had said after he passed the referee's course last fall.

GUIDED QUESTIONS

1 **From whose point of view is this story told?**

This story point of view is told from Derek.

2 **Predict how you think Mike will treat Derek since they are brothers.**

I think Derek will not help Mike and be fair.

3 **Explain why Mike doesn't want to be a referee for Derek's team. What does he have to do during this game?**

READING GUIDE

"That should make it easier. And I'll try not to ref your games, Derek. I don't want anyone to say I'm playing favorites."

Until now that plan had worked. As a first-year ref, he usually worked only a couple of games a weekend, mostly the younger teams. Until today, that is, when he'd got an early phone call. "The Winston twins both have the flu," he said when he hung up. "They were supposed to work several games. So I've got two more to do, including yours, Derek." He didn't look happy, but I didn't mind. I figured it could help our team.

"Just pretend you don't know him," my dad said, and I figured that's what Mike was doing now—ignoring me.

The game started off with a bang. The Redhawks scored in the first minute, but then we scored, too. A few minutes later we traded goals again.

"Two-two already!" Tony said as we skated to the bench. "Looks like a high-scoring game." But after that, things tightened up, and nobody else scored for a while.

Halfway through the second period, though, things started going badly. Tony accidentally tripped one of the Redhawk forwards, and Mike called him for a penalty. I gave Mike a dirty look and I was even madder when the
4 Redhawks scored on the power play.

"Not your fault, Tiny T," I called to Tony. "Let's get it back!"

"Go Gophers, go!" someone in the crowd shouted. "Go for the goal! Gopher the goal!"

We almost did! Ryan, our center, got the face-off and passed the puck across to me. I sped up the left side, faked a rush on the net, then snapped it back to Ryan. When the Redhawk defense moved to stop him, I skated in toward the net, and Ryan sent the puck back to me. I was just winding up when one of the Redhawk defensemen grabbed me from the side and knocked my stick away. I snatched at his stick, and we shoved at each other.

The whistle blew, and Mike called penalties on both of us. "That wasn't my fault!" I objected. "It was all him!"

GUIDED QUESTIONS

Why Mike does not want to referee because he does not want anyone to think he plays favorites with his [illegible] brother.

4 **What inference can you make about what Derek expected from his brother in this situation?**

Derek expected Mike to help him.

Go on to the next page

READING GUIDE

"Both of you!" Mike snapped. "And no arguing, or I'll give you more time."

From behind my mask I glared at him, then headed for the penalty box. "Some brother!" I muttered to myself. "Doesn't he have eyes?"

I sat in the penalty box, fuming until my time was up. Then Coach Andrews made me miss an extra shift. "Take some time to cool off, Derek," he said. "You shouldn't have
5 retaliated." I only go to play one more shift before the second period ended!

As we skated off for the intermission, Mike came up behind me. "Sorry, Derek," he said. "But remember what I said—no special treatment. If I'm the referee and you're
6 playing, you're not my brother."

I kept my back to him and did what he'd done earlier; I pretended I didn't hear him.

"Brothers!" I snapped as I got to the locker room.

"He was just doing his job," said Tony.

While we rested, Coach Andrews went over some of the plays, and we all listened carefully. "Let's get that next goal," he said as we headed back out, and the team started the "Gopher the goal!" chant.

My line took the first shift. The Redhawk center got the face-off and started in on our net, but Tony flipped the puck off his stick. "Pass it, Tiny!" I shouted, and he winged it at me.

I slid it over to Ryan, who took off up the ice on a breakaway and banged it into the Redhawks' net. There were high-fives all around!

7 With the score tied, both teams played more carefully. Then the Redhawks scored again, and the game got a little rougher.

With about ten minutes left, the Redhawks were forcing the play. I skated back to help our defense. As I neared Tony, he checked one of the big Redhawks, and they both went down in a heap. The next thing I knew, I'd tripped over a leg and crashed into the boards, shoulder first. I slid to the ice.

GUIDED QUESTIONS

5 What does *retaliated* mean? Use context clues to figure out its meaning. To return like for like and evil for evil.

6 Link the interaction between Derek and Mike to your own experiences. How do you think Derek feels every time Mike says, "You're not my brother?"

I think he feel that he does not care about him and his team losing.

7 What aspects of the plot keep you interested in the story and wanting to read on? What keeps me reading is if mike is going to help him at the end or not.

READING GUIDE

For a moment I lay there, my ears ringing. I started to sit up, and a sharp pain jabbed my shoulder. "Oooh!" I gasped and lay back down.

About then, Tony got untangled and leaned over me. "Are you hurt?" he asked.

8 I tried to sit up again, and a wave of pain shot down my arm and around my back. I gritted my teeth to keep from crying out.

Mike skated up. "Take it easy, Derek!" he said, kneeling beside me. "Don't move especially if it's your back."

"It's not my back," I said through clenched teeth. "It's my shoulder."

"Don't move, anyway, till someone looks at it." He stood up and waved for Coach Andrews. Everyone crowded around me.

9 "Back off," Mike ordered them. "Give my brother some room. It won't help to have you peering down at him."

I closed my eyes and took deep breaths while the coach examined my shoulder, but I couldn't control the pain or the water in my eyes.

"It's the shoulder, all right," Coach Andrews said. "Not your back, thank goodness."

After that, things were kind of a blur. I know Mike and Coach Andrews helped me skate off and get to the locker room. Mom was waiting for me there, and she took my skates. I left the rest of my equipment on, and she drove me straight to the hospital.

"A dislocated shoulder," the doctor said, once he'd got my hockey sweater and shoulder pads off. "You're lucky. That's easy to fix."

I didn't feel lucky; I felt like I was being stabbed!

"I have to pull your shoulder back into place," the doctor said. "I'll give you a sedative to help control the pain while I do it."

Before long I felt like I was floating in dreamland. I guess the needle put me out for a few minutes, and by the time I came to, the doctor had popped my shoulder back

GUIDED QUESTIONS

5 **Retell in your own words what has happened to Derek.**

What has happened is Derek has hurt is shoulder and back.

9 **Compare how Mike acts now that Derek is hurt to how he treated Derek throughout the game.**

He treats him with attention because he sees his brother is hurt and he treats him with a lot of treatment not speacial but enough to let him know he is not cheating.

Go on to the next page

READING GUIDE

into its socket. The pain—at least ninety percent of it—had gone.

"It'll be tender for a few days," the doctor said. "No hockey for a week or so."

I dozed on the drive home and for an hour or two afterward. When I awoke, Mike was beside me.

"Your getting hurt inspired Tony," he said. "He got a goal. The game ended in a tie."

"Good," I said. "It was a good game." I paused, remembering other things. "I thought you said when I'm on the ice, I'm not your brother. How about when I was hurt?"

"I said when you're playing hockey, you aren't my brother," he said with a grin. "You weren't playing then, were you?"

10 I grinned back.

Sample Extended Response Question

11 Think about the way Mike acts toward Derek during the game. Consider his responsibilities as a referee and as a brother. Do you think he acts appropriately? Why or why not? Support your answer with examples from the story.

GUIDED QUESTIONS

10 What does this story tell you about brothers?

11 Connect this question to your own life. How do you think a referee should act? How should a brother act? What would you have done in Mike's situation?

Activity **Directions** Answer the extended-response question. Use the lines below.

A. I think the way mike act toward the game and Mike was approppricately because he know as a referee it was not right to play favorites so he played fair towards everyone and on court it is a whole different thing, Because on court it's only Refree and players not Brothers Or anything else.

Why I say that is because in the story Mike treats his brother as if he doesn't Know him but of the ice he treats him as his brother.

Self Evaluation

Ask yourself:

- Did I explain the responsibilities of a referee?
- Did I explain how Mike treats Derek?
- Did I agree or disagree with it?
- Did I use details from the story to support my answer?
- Is my answer clearly written and well organized?

How Your Response Will Be Evaluated

Your answer will be evaluated on a scale from 0-4. Aim to write a response that receives a 4. Teachers will use this rubric to evaluate your answer.

Extended-Response Rubric

Score	Criteria
4	● Provides extensive evidence of the kind of interpretation called for in the item or question ● Is well organized, elaborate, and thorough ● Demonstrates a complete understanding of the whole work as well as how the parts blend to form the whole ● Is relevant, comprehensive, and detailed, demonstrating a thorough understanding of the reading selection ● Addresses thoroughly the important elements of the question ● Contains logical reasoning and communicates effectively and clearly *(A four-point response may go beyond the requirements of the item.)*
3	● Provides evidence that essential interpretation has been made ● Is thoughtful and reasonably accurate ● Indicates an understanding of the concept or item ● Communicates adequately, and generally reaches reasonable conclusions ● Contains some combination of the following flaws: ◆ Minor flaws in reasoning or interpretation ◆ Failure to address some aspect of the item or omission of some detail
2	● Is mostly accurate and relevant ● Contains some combination of the following flaws: ◆ Incomplete evidence of interpretation ◆ Unsubstantiated statements made about the text ◆ Incomplete understanding of the concept or item ◆ Lack of comprehensiveness, faulty reasoning, unclear communication

1	● Provides little evidence of interpretation ● Is unorganized and incomplete ● Exhibits decoding rather than reading ● Demonstrates a partial understanding of the item, but is sketchy and unclear ● Indicates some effort beyond restating the item ● Contains some combination of the following flaws: ◆ Little understanding of the concept or item ◆ Failure to address most aspects of the item ◆ Inability to make coherent meaning from the text

0	● Shows no understanding of the item or student fails to respond to item

Question

Think about the way Mike acts toward Derek during the game. Consider his responsibilities as a referee and as a brother. Do you think he acts appropriately? Why or why not? Support your answer with examples from the story.

Sample Response

A referee must act fairly toward both teams. Mike refuses to give Derek any special treatment just because they are brothers. In fact, when Derek says hello to Mike before the game starts, Mike actually ignores him. As the game proceeds, Mike refuses to favor Derek and gives Derek a penalty. When Derek gets hurt however, Mike is right there to help. He is in a position of authority as a referee, but he also helps Derek when Derek is injured.

Although it's easy to be angry with Mike, deep down I know that he is right in acting the way that he does. He can't possibly be a good referee if he favors his brother. He would also jeopardize his job as a referee if anyone thought that he was playing favorites. Naturally, I want Mike to treat Derek better, but I know that he is just doing his job. When he helps Derek when Derek dislocates his shoulder, I see that Mike truly cares about Derek as a brother should.

Activity

Directions Exchange your response with a partner. Using the scoring rubric, evaluate your partner's response and give it a score. Be ready to explain why the response received the score you gave to it.

____

____

____

____

____

Lesson 20 Proofreading Practice

Once you have written your extended response, you should proofread it. Check it for errors in order to correct any mistakes. Look for errors in:

- spelling
- punctuation
- grammar
- mechanics

Directions The passage you are about to read contains twenty errors. Underline or circle each error and correct it.

A referee has an important job to do. His mane goal is to referee the game in a fair and unbiased manner. This means that he can't favor won team over another team, or even one player over another player. In the story, "Brothers on Ice," Mike, the referee for the hockey game, has a truly difficult job to do. As a first-year ref, he has to prove himself as a good referee while remaining unbiased towards the Grantly Gophers the team that his own brother Derek is playing on.

Activity continued

Derek, of course, expects Mike to give him some special treatment. Mike and their Dad, however, makes it clear that Mike will not play favorites. This is hard for Derek to believe since Mike is his brother. But as the game begins, Derek sees that Mike plans to pretend that he doesn't have a special relationship with Derek. Even gives Derek a penalty. Although the Gophers need help, Mike won't give them special treatment. He wants to play fair.

A person reading this story would naturally be disturbed by Mikes behavior. The reader wants Mike to help Derek. After all, they have a blood relationship. But intellectually, we know that Mike is doing the right thing. One lesson that this story teaches is that we can know that something is right even though it may not feel write.

Independent Practice for the Test

Read the story below and answer the questions that follow. You will complete multiple-choice questions, a short-response question, and an extended-response question.

Tinker's Tide

by Marcy Barack

Josie tasted salt in the corners of her mouth. She couldn't tell if it came from the tears on her cheeks, from the sweat on Tinker's neck, or from the wind blowing off the bay.

Digging her toe in the sand, Josie leaned against her steaming mare. "Only a week left," she whispered as she watched the water surge across the flats.

Twice a day, the strongest tides in the world filled and emptied the Bay of Fundy. The brief Canadian summers brought tourists bearing Brownie cameras to pose on the rock pillars and to clamber through the cave carved by the tide. That summer of 1958, Josie rode out every day to catch the tide. The rest of the time she was saddled with responsibilities.

The Atlantic Ocean rippled before Josie like a magic carpet. She wished it would carry Tinker and her away before Papa came home to sell the horses.

The thought of losing Tinker stung Josie's eyes. She jumped on the mare's back and turned her toward the salt marsh bordering the bay.

Long-legged birds poked their sharp beaks into the ground, searching for frogs and snakes. Black-and-white cows chomped on the tall grass.

As the sun rose over the sea of grass, Josie and Tinker picked their way through the seabirds and cattle. Josie had milked her share of cows before dawn.

Like a great green quilt, the marsh was threaded with a network of dikes raised by Josie's ancestors. A rider waved at Josie from a low ridge ahead.

Josie joined her sister Margie on the dike path. "We're waiting for you," Margie whined with worry.

Josie reached down to pat Tinker's strong brown shoulder. "Well, I'm here. Now if the six of us put our heads together, maybe we'll think of a way to save the horses."

Josie's brothers and sisters clustered by the busy road that led to the tidal caves. Across the blacktop, their sunny yellow farmhouse and big red barn backed up against the deep green hills.

Go On

Josie tethered Tinker beside the other horses. Five faces looked up to Josie as she sat down. "I talked to Papa before he left to cut timber," she began.

"Why'd he go?" interrupted Dorothy.

Josie gathered the little girl into her lap. "For the wages, Dorothy. These are hard times. That's why Papa can't afford to keep the horses."

"But Tinker's the only horse we had to pay for," said Margie. "She gave us our mounts free." Margie's horse, like all the others tied to the fence, was Tinker's offspring.

"Horses cost money to keep," Josie explained. "Cows bring in money. If we get rid of the horses, we'll have room in the barn for more cows, and we'll make more money."

"I've got a loose tooth," Patrick, one of the twins, wiggled it for everyone to see. "When the tooth fairy comes, I'll give the money to Papa."

Jeannette, Patrick's twin sister, fingered the cross dangling from a delicate chain around her neck.

"This Sunday at Mass I'll pray for God to save the horses."

"Father Joseph says God helps those who help themselves," William reminded them in his deepening voice. "I'm big enough to get a job haying."

"The grass won't be ready to cut again until the end of the summer," Margie pointed out. "Too late for us."

Everyone looked back at Josie.

"I have to stay home to help Mama. The new baby's due soon."

The kids fell silent.

The horses' ears flicked forward as a sleek new station wagon pulled off the road next to them.

Josie jumped up, welcoming the distraction. "May I help you?"

The driver rolled down his window, "Hello, young lady," he said. "Is this the way to the caves?"

"Straight ahead eight kilometers. But the tide's in now. The caves are flooded."

"Oh no!" cried the woman beside him. "We came all this way to see them!"

Josie peered inside. A boy and girl pouted in the back seat, just like the glum circle of kids on the grass. Josie wanted to cheer them up, all of them. "Would your kids like to pet the horses?"

The children squealed with delight and scrambled out of the car. William lifted the little boy to pat Tinker on the nose. Margie showed the girl how to hold her hand flat to feed the horses an apple.

Josie smiled as she watched the children mingle, happy around the horses. That's how she felt chasing the tide with Tinker. "They could ride if they'd like," she said to the parents.

"Oh, yes!" The little boy crowed.

The girl grabbed the man's hand. "Please, may we, Daddy?" she begged.

Josie took a deep breath. "It's a dollar each."

Margie gasped. The twins hauled Josie aside. Brothers and sisters buzzed around her.

"You can't ask for money."

"They won't pay to ride."

"What will Mama say?"

Josie shushed them all. "If the horses can pay their way, Papa might let us keep them. I'll run ask Mama."

Josie hurried across the road while the man and woman talked quietly with each other. When she returned, she caught the anxious eyes of her brothers and sisters, and nodded.

The man and woman turned to face them. "We'd like to go, too," said the man, pulling out his wallet.

The horses swung their heads at the cheers that erupted from the children.

Josie, riding Tinker, led the visitors across the marsh. While they were gone, the kids made a sign and tacked it to the fence: HORSEBACK RIDES $1. The grass by the road was soon worn flat by cars full of adults eager to stretch their legs while their children played cowboy.

When Papa returned a week later, the children handed him seventy-five dollars.

In ten years, the cows were gone; the barn was filled with horses. And Josie and Tinker still galloped across the marsh every day to catch the tide.

Go On

1. Which choice BEST explains why "Tinker's Tide" is an appropriate title for this story?
   A. Tinker's luck comes in, just like the tide.
   B. Tinker lives near the shore.
   C. Tinker plays in the tide all day with Josie.
   D. The horse is named Tinker.

2. What problem has made Josie quite upset?
   A. She can't succeed at any job she tries.
   B. She doesn't want to lose Tinker.
   C. She doesn't want to help take care of her mother's new baby.
   D. She wants to charge for horseback rides.

3. Which of the following choices does NOT describe Josie?
   A. sensitive and emotional
   B. motivated and inspired
   C. irresponsible and easygoing
   D. smart and clever

4. Why does Josie charge money for the horseback ride?
   A. The people in the station wagon insist on riding.
   B. She wants to raise money so that they won't sell Tinker.
   C. She wants her father to come home and not have to cut timber.
   D. She wants to buy cows.

5. What can you infer happened at the end of the story?

   A. Josie's father let them keep Tinker, since no one wanted to buy Tinker.

   B. The children made enough money to keep the horses.

   C. The cows died.

   D. Father got angry with Josie for charging for horseback rides.

6. What theme or message about life do you think the author wants to convey in this story?

   What message he wants to give us about life is when you want something you have to work hard and everything is not going to come easily.

7. Retell what happens in this story. Focus on the problem that Josie faces and the solution to the problem.

   The problem that Josie faces is that they are not making enough money and they can't sale any cows so they are going to sale Tinker, but then Josie made signs for horse back riding and it cost $1 per ride, so people started to come and ride the horse. So by time her dad got back they had enough money to keep Tinker and they sold all the cows, and also had barn filled with horses.

Workshop

Activity

Directions Consider each theme listed in the first column of the chart. What books, short stories, plays, or folk tales have you read that have these themes? Write the title of a piece of fiction with this theme in the second column of the chart.

Theme	Title
the struggle for survival	
appreciating oneself	
good versus evil	
things are not always the way they seem	

Home Involvement Activities

Book Cards

When you read a good book, share it with others! After each member of your family reads a book, ask that person to fill out a book card. Make book cards out of index cards and keep them in a flip-top box such as a recipe card holder. On each card, write the following information:

- Title of the book
- Author's name
- Type of book (novel, science fiction, short stories, mystery, play, etc.)
- Number of pages
- Brief summary of the book
- Why you would recommend it or not recommend it
- The family member who you think would most enjoy the book

Read a Play

Choose a play that would appeal to the different members of your family and read it together. Assign each family member a role or consider changing roles after each scene or act. Decide how often you will read the play together (unless you will read the whole play in one sitting) and how much of the play you will read at each session.

Write a Mystery Story

Have you heard the old saying that two heads are better than one? Try putting your heads together to create a plot for a mystery story. Brainstorm to think of different ideas and work together to write an intriguing plot.

Chapter 2 Reading Poetry

What's Coming Up?

In this chapter, you will learn:

- what poetry is
- strategies and skills for reading poetry
- how to answer multiple-choice questions
- how to analyze words that are used both as nouns and as verbs
- how to compare and contrast
- how to critique and evaluate a poem
- how to write a short response
- how to recommend a poem
- how to connect a poem's content to the author's purpose
- how to build your vocabulary
- how to write an extended response
- how to proofread

Does This Sound Familiar?

- You're at a school dance, and as you move your feet you listen to the singer's words. Song lyrics are poems.
- You and a friend are making up raps in which each of you claims to be the greatest. You're already writing and performing poems!
- Mother's Day is coming up. What's a good gift for your Mom? You look through a gift shop and find a little book of inspiring poems.
- While you're at it, *you* need a Mother's Day card, too. The one you like best has four lines of writing inside. To your amazement, the name underneath the writing is William Shakespeare. You're already reading the greatest poet in English! And you can understand him!

Lesson 2 How to Read Poetry

When you read poems, you will often ask yourself what they mean. At school, questions about poems' meanings will appear on tests and in discussions. Use the following strategies and skills to get at the meanings of the poems you read.

Keys To Success

APPLY READING STRATEGIES

Set a Purpose

Your purpose is your reason for reading. It gives your reading a direction. Be aware of your purpose, and keep it in mind as you read.

Make, Confirm, and Revise Predictions

You've probably practiced making predictions while reading fiction. Adapt the same strategy to reading poetry. In poetry, "what happens next" might not be an event in a plot. It might be an emotion that the speaker feels, or an idea the poet expresses. You can still make educated guesses about where the poem is going; you can see whether those guesses are right or wrong; and you can revise any wrong ones.

Retell

Here's another strategy that can be adapted from fiction. Pause every so often to tell yourself what has been said so far in the poem. Remember that in a poem, the things that happen aren't always as clear-cut as in a story.

Summarize

A summary contains only the most important facts or events about the poem, and no minor details. Unlike a retelling, a summary is always much shorter than the original. It might be only two or three sentences long.

Connect Important Ideas

Everything in a poem is there for a reason. Approach the poem like a detective, asking yourself, "What does this line up here have to do with that line down there?" Every so often, you might feel an "Aha!" of understanding.

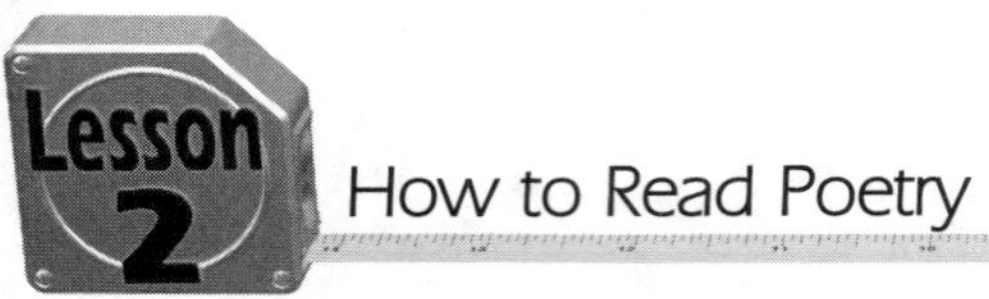

How to Read Poetry

Link Ideas to Your Own Experience and Knowledge

You'll be more open to understanding a poem if you can link the experiences, ideas, and feelings in it to things you already know. Have you ever felt the way the speaker of the poem feels? (You might be surprised how often the answer is, "Yes.")

Form Pictures

In most poems, something is being described. Try to see or hear or feel it in your mind.

Check Your Understanding

Most good readers stop several times while reading a poem, in order to think about what they've read and ask themselves whether they understand it. Simply rereading a passage, or a whole poem, is a very effective way to increase your understanding of it. Rereading and asking questions is even more powerful. Two other good tactics are looking up unfamiliar words and skimming ahead for a preview.

Make Inferences

An inference is an educated guess made with the support of details. Poets choose their details very carefully so that each detail means something. Again, use the detective method: each detail is a clue to "solving" the poem.

Compare and Contrast

When you compare things, you find ways in which they are similar. When you contrast things, you find ways in which they are different. A poet may use comparison and contrast to highlight an idea or feeling. A reader may compare and contrast things in a poem to things in real life, or to things in a different poem.

Use Context Clues

In reading poetry, you may come across some words you don't know. Get into the habit of trying to figure out their meanings by looking at the surrounding passage—the context. Take a guess. Then check your guess in a dictionary.

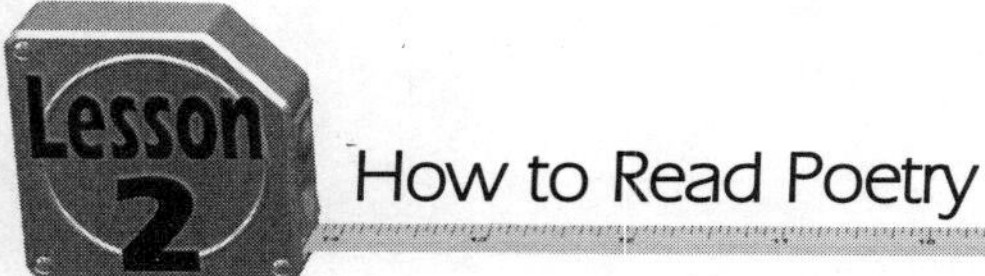

LOOK FOR ELEMENTS OF LITERATURE

Rhythm

Poetry has its roots in music, and music has rhythm, or beat. Language has rhythm, too. The sentences you speak every day in casual conversation have rhythms. You stress some words and syllables and not others. However, when you speak, or when you write prose, the rhythm of the words is probably not very important to you. That's a huge part of what makes poetry different from prose. In poetry, rhythm is very important. Rhythmic language sounds more intense than ordinary language, and a poem's rhythm can affect its mood. Some poems have a regular beat, or meter. In other poems, the rhythm is more subtle.

Rhyme

Rhyme is a specific kind of repetition of vowel sounds. When two words rhyme, the last accented vowel sound in each word is the same, and all the sounds after those vowel sounds are also the same. *Catch* and *match* rhyme, because both have short *a* as their last accented vowel sound. (Actually, it's their only vowel sound.) *Catching* and *matching* rhyme. They both have short *a* as their last accented vowel sound, and the sounds that follow are also the same in both words. But *catching* and *matchbox* don't rhyme. The last accented vowel sound is the same in both words, but the sounds that follow it are not identical.

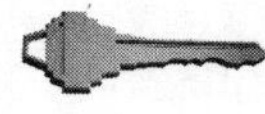

Figurative Language

Figurative language is a kind of comparison between two things that are basically not alike. The words of the comparison are not literal facts. For example, if you say, "It feels like the North Pole out here," it doesn't mean that in the place where you are, the temperature is the same as at the North Pole. It's just a figure of speech meaning that you feel very cold.

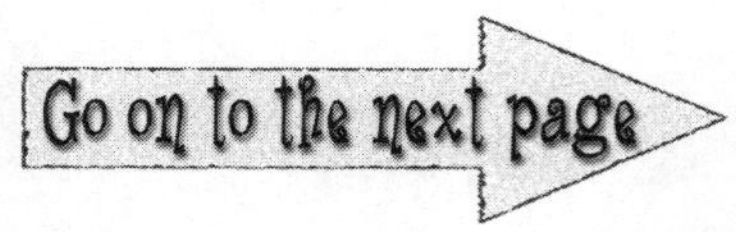

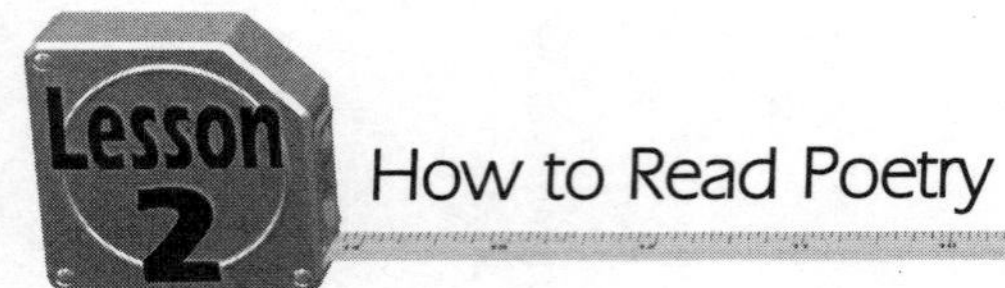

Three kinds of figurative language often found in poetry are **simile**, **metaphor**, and **personification**.

A **simile** compares things by using connecting words such as *like*, *as*, *than*, or *resembles*. For example, "He arrived for dinner as *hungry as a grubworm in a pile of trash*." The simile highlights a new, interesting way of seeing the things that are being compared. (Did you ever think of your dinner guest as a grubworm?)

In a **metaphor**, linking words such as *like* or *as* are not used. This makes the connection between the two objects seem stronger. The two things are not just *like* each other, in a sense they are each other. Here's a familiar metaphor: "*A blanket of snow* lay over the land." A real blanket cannot be made out of snow. Real snow on the ground is not a piece of cloth that warms a sleeping person. But the metaphor makes the snow seem to be a blanket. In fact, the metaphor makes something cold seem warm!

In **personification**, something nonhuman is described as if it were human. For example, "The sun smiled down upon the happy farmlands." There are two personifications in that sentence. The sun is smiling like a person, and the farmlands are happy like a person. In reality, the sun does not smile and land is neither happy nor sad.

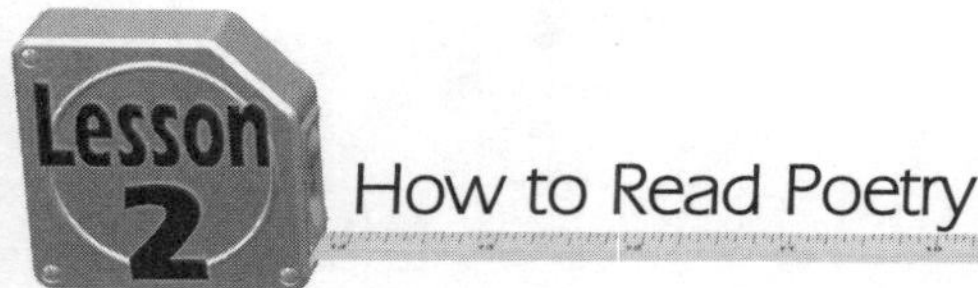

How to Read Poetry

READING GUIDE

Directions Use your key strategies to help you follow the poem below. Use the questions to keep yourself aware of the strategies.

My Brother Bert

—Ted Hughes

Pets are the hobby of my brother Bert.
1 He used to go to school with a mouse in his shirt.

His hobby it grew, as some hobbies will,
And grew and GREW and GREW until—

Oh don't breathe a word, pretend you haven't heard.
2 A simply appalling thing has occurred—

The very thought makes me iller and iller:
3 Bert's brought home a gigantic gorilla!

If you think that's really not such a scare,
What if it quarrels with his grizzly bear?

You still think you could keep your head?
What if the lion from under the bed

And the four ostriches that deposit
4 Their football eggs in his bedroom closet

And the aardvark out of his bottom drawer
5 All danced out and joined in the roar?

6 What if the pangolins were to caper
Out of their nests behind the wallpaper?

With the fifty sorts of bats
7 That hang on his hatstand like old hats,

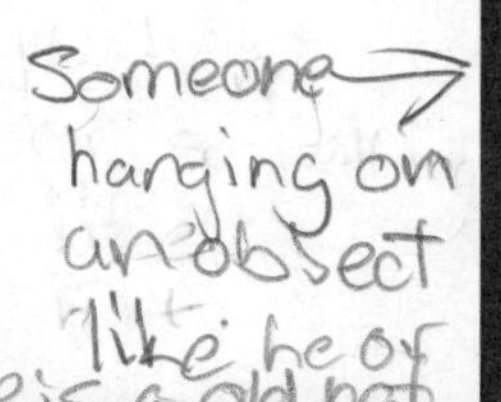

GUIDED QUESTIONS

1 What do you **predict** a poem in which a brother goes to school with a mouse in his shirt will be about?

2 Look for **rhythms** and **rhymes** in the poem, reading aloud to hear them. What do you find?

3 Is your **prediction confirmed**? If not, *revise* it.

4 What kind of **figurative language** is *football eggs,* and what does it mean?

5 **Form pictures** of the scene. What do you see?

6 What word or words give you a possible **context clue** to the meaning of *pangolins?* Make sure to check the meaning in a dictionary.

7 What kind of **figurative language** is *hang on his hatstand like old hats*? What does it mean?

Go on to the next page

READING GUIDE

And out of a shoebox the excitable platypus
8 Along with the ocelot or jungle-cattypus?

9 The wombat, the dingo, the gecko, the grampus—
How they would shake the house with their rumpus!

Not to forget the bandicoot
10 Who would certainly peer from his battered old boot.

Why it could be a dreadful day,
11 And what, oh what, would the neighbors say!

GUIDED QUESTIONS

8 **Check your understanding**: what could *jungle-cattypus* mean? Is it a real word?
It is not a real word.

9 **Make an inference**—what is a wombat, dingo, gecko, and grampus?

10 **Retell** the poem in your own words. Then reduce your retelling to a brief **summary.**

11 **Link Ideas to Your Own Experience and Knowledge:** Does the last line sound familiar?
NO it does not.

Fluency Tip

If you have trouble pronouncing some of the names of unfamiliar animals in this poem, try reading them aloud in context, so that their names fit in with the rhythms and rhymes.

10. The poem is basicly about animals that are supernatural and very real in the real world.

9. wombat - mammals that represent a small bear,
dingo - A wild dog of Australia.
gecko - A small tropical lizard.
grampus - A sea mammal that relates and resembles a Dolphin.

How to Answer Multiple-Choice Questions

What's Expected on the Test?

One of the selections you read on the Ohio Proficiency Test might be a poem. You will be asked questions about the poem, and some of the questions will probably be multiple-choice. Try to recall and use the following strategies when answering multiple-choice questions.

Test-Taking Strategies

Do the Easy Ones First

What if you're stumped by a hard question, but you can tell that the question after it is easier? Go ahead to the easier one first, then return to the harder one. This will give you more time to think about the harder question.

Eliminate Wrong Choices

Even if you aren't sure about an answer right away, you may be able to narrow down the possibilities. Look for choices that are clearly wrong, and eliminate those at the start. Then, you'll be left with fewer possible choices.

Guess!

On the Ohio Proficiency Test you should answer every question, whether you know the answer or not. You don't get any credit for leaving an answer blank. Of course, it's better to know an answer than not to know it. But if there's a question you just can't figure out, pick an answer on a hunch. At least you'll have some chance of getting it right.

Review Your Work

Double-check your work by rereading the questions and the answers. Does your answer still sound right?

Avoid Careless Errors

The most frustrating thing is to be marked wrong when you really knew the answer. Make sure you don't give any wrong answers by accident. Make sure that you read all questions, answers, and instructions carefully. Don't overlook any tricky little words such as *not*. Make sure that if you meant to fill in A, you really filled in A and not B. And check to be sure you didn't accidentally skip any questions or mark the answer for one question in the space for another question.

Go on to the next page

How to Answer Multiple-Choice Questions

Sample Multiple-Choice Questions

Directions Try your hand at answering these multiple-choice questions about "My Brother Bert." Reread the poem before you begin. After you have answered the questions, turn to page 125 to check your responses.

1. What do *deposit* and *closet* have in common that *drawer* and *roar* also have in common?

A. They have the same number of letters.

B. They are the poet's favorite words.

C. Each pair rhymes.

D. All four words rhyme with one another.

2. Which of the following is a figurative expression?

A. the aardvark out of his bedroom drawer

B. the wombat, the dingo, the gecko, the grampus

C. the ocelot or jungle-cattypus

D. hang on his hatstand like old hats

3. "Pets are the hobby of my brother Bert" is a line in the poem. It is also a

A. sentence.

B. stanza.

C. simile.

D. personification.

4. "My Brother Bert" is a narrative poem but not a ballad, because

A. it expresses the deep feelings of the speaker.

B. it doesn't tell a story, but it rhymes.

C. it tells a story, but it doesn't repeat passages the way a song does.

D. it is not about a pirate, king, outlaw, or similar colorful character.

5. Why do you think Ted Hughes included animals such as pangolins, bandicoots, aardvarks, wombats, dingoes, geckoes, and grampuses in the poem?

A. He is interested in the unusual habits of these animals.

B. He wanted to report factually all the animals that his brother Bert collected.

C. He is an expert on rare zoo creatures and wanted to educate students about them.

D. He thought their names were funny.

Check Your Answers

How close did you come to aceing this sample test? Check your answers.

1. What do *deposit* and *closet* have in common that *drawer* and *roar* also have in common?
   - **A. INCORRECT** They do not have the same number of letters.
   - **B. INCORRECT** The poem does not present any evidence about what the poet's favorite words are. The mere fact that they are in the poem is not evidence of that.
   - **C. CORRECT** *Deposit* rhymes with *closet*, and *drawer* rhymes with *roar*.
   - **D. INCORRECT** The words in one pair do not rhyme with the words in the other pair.

2. Which of the following is a figurative expression?
   - **A. INCORRECT** An aardvark in a bedroom drawer is unusual, but it isn't figurative: it's a literal description.
   - **B. INCORRECT** These are just four names of animals—nothing figurative about that!
   - **C. INCORRECT** *Cattypus* is a made-up, comical word, but that doesn't make it figurative.
   - **D. CORRECT** In this simile, bats are compared to hats hanging from a hatstand.

3. "Pets are the hobby of my brother Bert" is a line in the poem. It is also a
   - **A. CORRECT** In this poem, the first line is also one complete sentence.
   - **B. INCORRECT** It is possible to have a one-line stanza, but this line isn't separated from other lines as a stanza would be.
   - **C. INCORRECT** The line is a literal statement that doesn't involve a comparison.
   - **D. INCORRECT** Same reason as for C; also, although there is a person in the line, nothing else is compared to the person.

4. "My Brother Bert" is a narrative poem but not a ballad, because

A. INCORRECT A poem that expresses the deep feelings of the speaker is a lyrical poem.

B. INCORRECT It does tell a story: the story of Bert's animal collection.

C. CORRECT This narrative has rhyme and rhythm, but not the repetition of entire lines or key phrases that is found in ballads.

D. INCORRECT Many old ballads are about pirates, kings, outlaws, or similar colorful characters, but not every ballad has to be.

5. Why do you think Ted Hughes included animals such as pangolins, bandicoots, aardvarks, wombats, dingoes, geckoes, and grampuses in the poem?

A. INCORRECT Actually, the poem tells very little about the habits of these animals.

B. INCORRECT The poem is not factual!

C. INCORRECT There is no evidence that the poet is an expert on rare zoo animals, and anyway, the poem provides little education about them.

D. CORRECT Yes! It's a comic poem, and one way poets make their poems comical is by using words that make readers laugh or smile. Did you think this answer was too silly to be right?

Word Analysis

Words Used as Nouns and Verbs

Most nouns are just nouns and most verbs are just verbs. But some words are both, depending on how they're used. For example:

> **run** (*noun*): a score in baseball
> **run** (*verb*): to move very quickly using the legs
>
> **fly** (*noun*): a type of winged insect
> **fly** (*verb*): to travel through the air
> **fly** (*oops, another baseball noun*): a ball that is hit a long way into the air

The way to tell which meaning of a word applies is to check the *context*—the words and phrases surrounding it. Knowing the overall meaning of the passage, you can zero in on the specific usage of the word.

Also, use clues of sentence structure to figure out whether a word is being used as a noun or a verb. If a word is preceded by an article such as *a*, *an*, or *the*, it is probably a noun. If a word is preceded by *to* without an article, it is probably a verb.

Activity

Directions Read the poem and answer the questions.

Pigeons

—Eve Merriam

Other birds soar in the clouds

these are city dwellers
they see the sky
only between clumps of buildings

they nest on fire escapes
air conditioners
basement stoops

they can nest on nails

they are gray and bedraggled
they flap their wings in the midst of filth
and they make more filth

they are noisy
they are disgusting
they have an iridescent beauty

they huddle they survive

Activity continued

1. How can *clouds* be both a noun and a verb? Which is it in this poem?

   The clouds can be a noun because it is a thing and a verb if something happened to it. It is a noun.

2. How can *flap* be both a noun and a verb? Which is it in this poem?

   It can be a verb because something is moving or happening to the wings, it can be a noun because it is a word of a noun. It is a verb.

3. How can *nest* be both a noun and a verb? Which is it in this poem?

   A nest can be a noun because it's a thing and it can be a verb because it could be someone nest someone or something up.

4. How can *huddle* be both a noun and a verb? Which is it in this poem?

   It can be a verb because it is a action or something moving and how it can be a noun is by being something that can move so it could be a thing.

5. Think of another word, not in this poem, that can be both a noun and a verb. State the word and explain its uses.

   A Bird can be a noun because it's a thing and how it can be a verb by it flying because it is action or something is happening when it moves.

Go on to the next page

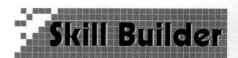

1. The noun *nail* means a small metal spike that is used to fasten pieces of wood; the verb *nail* means
   - **A.** fasten together.
   - **B.** make out of wood.
   - **C.** make out of metal.
   - **D.** loosen.

2. The noun *disgust* means a feeling of distaste; the verb *disgust* means to
   - **A.** hate someone else.
   - **B.** cause someone to feel distaste.
   - **C.** destroy.
   - **D.** make a horrible sound.

3. Which of the following words is NOT both a noun and a verb?
   - **A.** fire
   - **B.** escape
   - **C.** stoop
   - **D.** iridescent

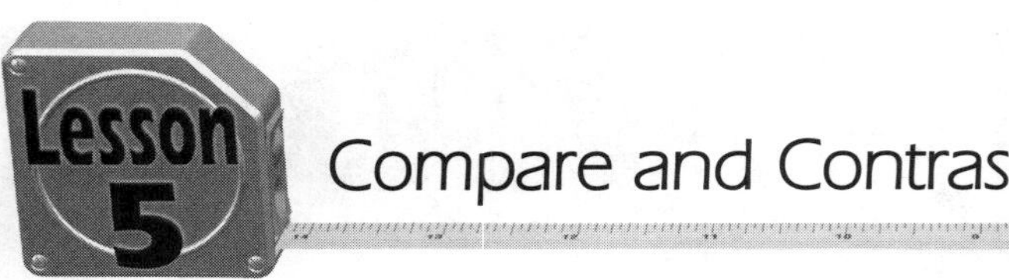

Compare and Contrast

Compare and Contrast

When you compare two things, you say how they are alike. For example, both poetry and prose are types of literature that can be beautiful. When you contrast two things, you say how they are different. For example, the choice of exactly the right word is more important in poetry than in prose.

Comparisons and contrasts are found often in poetry, especially in figurative language. Simile, metaphor, and pesonification are forms of comparison. If a poet can compare the subject of his or her poem to something unexpected, it gives delight to the reader. It can also give the reader a new, deeper way of seeing and thinking about the subjects of the comparison.

Activity

Directions Read the following poem and answer the questions.

Simile: Willow and Ginkgo

—Eve Merriam

The willow is like an etching,
Fine-lined against the sky.
The ginkgo is like a crude sketch,
Hardly worthy to be signed.

The willow's music is like a soprano,
Delicate and thin.
The ginkgo's tune is like a chorus
With everyone joining in.

The willow is like a nymph with streaming hair;
Wherever it grows, there is green and gold and fair.
The willow dips to the water,
Protected and precious, like the king's favorite daughter.

Go on to the next page

Activity continued

The ginkgo forces its way through gray concrete;
Like a city child, it grows up in the street.
Thrust against the metal sky,
Somehow it survives and even thrives.

My eyes feast upon the willow,
But my heart goes to the ginkgo.

1. State one way in which the ginkgo and the willow are alike.

2. According to the poet, how are the sounds of the willow and the ginkgo different?

3. The willow's branches are "like silken thread," while the ginkgo's branches are "like stubby rough wool." Is that a comparison or a contrast, and why?

4. The poem's last two lines contrast the poet's feelings about the two trees. Restate the contrast in your own words.

5. Why do you think the poem is called "Simile: Willow and Ginkgo" instead of just "Willow and Ginkgo"?

1. What overall contrast between the willow and the ginkgo does the poet express?

   A. The willow grows by the water, while the ginkgo grows on dry land.

   B. She likes the willow, but she dislikes the ginkgo.

   C. The willow is a European tree, while the ginkgo is an Asian tree.

   D. The willow is slim and delicate, while the ginkgo is tough and sturdy.

2. In the poem, two kinds of trees are compared to

   A. gold and silver.

   B. dancers.

   C. kinds of cloth.

   D. artwork.

3. In line 15, what is compared to metal?

   A. the sky

   B. a child

   C. the willow

   D. the ginkgo

Critique and Evaluate

When you critique and evaluate a poem, you make judgments about how good a poem it is. You reread it carefully and decide how well the poet has used specific literary elements. In other words, how successfully has the poet said what he or she wanted to say?

As you'll recall from Lesson 2, the literary elements of poetry include rhythm, rhyme, and figurative language. Figurative language may include simile, metaphor, and personification.

Activity

A. **Directions** Read the following poem and answer the questions.

December Leaves

—Kaye Starbird

The fallen leaves are cornflakes
That fill the lawn's wide dish,
And night and noon
The wind's a spoon
That stirs them with a swish.

The sky's a silver sifter,
A-sifting white and slow,
That gentle shakes
On crisp brown flakes
The sugar known as snow.

1. What figurative comparisons does the poet use in this poem? What is being compared to what?

____

____

Activity continued

2. What specific kind of figurative language is being used throughout the poem?

3. Successful figurative language is original and makes the reader see the subject in a new way. Also, successful figurative language helps the poet create an appropriate tone and mood. Do you think figurative language is used successfully in this poem? Why or why not?

4. Give an example of rhyme and an example of rhythm from this poem.

5. Do you think rhythm and rhyme are used effectively in this poem? Support your opinion with specific references.

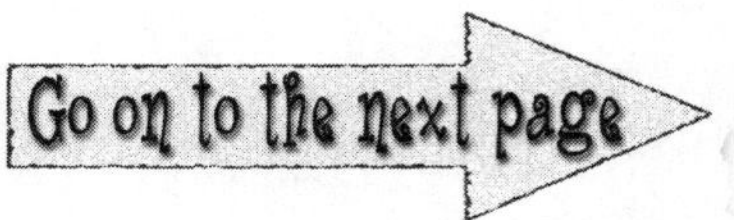
Go on to the next page

Activity

B. **Directions** Read the following poem and answer the questions.

Tuning Up

—Felice Holman

I'm at a concert
And the tuba moans.
    The tuba moans
And the bassoon groans.
    The bassoon groans
And the violin sings.
    The violin sings
And the cymbal rings.
    The cymbal rings
And the trumpet toots.
    The trumpet toots
And the flutist flutes.
    The flutist flutes
And the drummer drums.
    The drummer drums
And the cello hums. . . .
Then ending all this dissonance
The baton raps and starts to dance.

Activity continued

1. In your own words, state what this poem describes. Use specific details.

____

____

2. In your opinion, what is the most effective description of an instrument in this poem? Why?

____

____

3. In your opinion, what is the least effective description of an instrument in this poem? Why?

____

____

4. In what specific way does the poem use repetition?

____

____

5. In your opinion, is the repetition effecive or not? Explain your view.

____

____

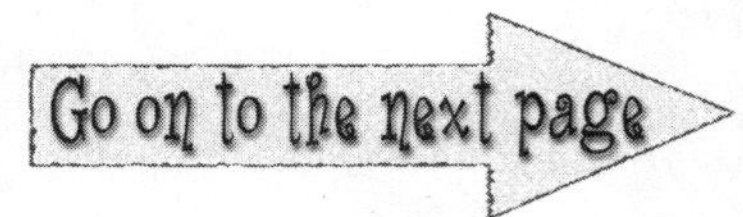

1. A reader who thinks "December Leaves" is a fine poem probably likes the use of

   A. plot.

   B. character.

   C. comparison.

   D. flashback.

2. A reader who thinks "Tuning Up" is a fine poem probably likes the way it uses words to describe

   A. sounds.

   B. people.

   C. the clarinet.

   D. the poet's thoughts.

3. What kind of person would probably give both "December Leaves" and "Tuning Up" a very positive evaluation?

   A. someone who likes fiction

   B. someone who likes rhyme and meter

   C. someone who likes love poems

   D. someone who likes ballads

Directions: Read the selection and answer the questions.

The Pedalling Man

—by Russell Hoban

And the pedalling man knew what to do–
He just pedalled, yes he pedalled:
He rode through the night with the wind just right
And he rode clear into the morning,
Riding easy, riding breezy, riding
Slow in the sunrise and the wind out of the east.

A weathervane was what he was–
Cast-iron man with a sheet-iron propeller, riding a
Worm gear, holding a little steering wheel,
Iron legs pumping up and down–show him a
Wind and he'd go. Work all day and
All his pay was the weather. Nights, too,
We'd lie in bed and hear him
Creak up there in the dark as he
Swung into the wind and worked up speed,
Humming and thrumming so you could
Feel it all through the house–
The more wind, the faster he went, right through
Spring, summer, and fall.

He rode warm winds out of the south,
Wet winds out of the east, and the
Dry west winds, rode them all with a
Serious iron face. Hard-nosed, tight-mouthed
Yankee-looking kind of an iron man.
"Show me a wind and I'll go," he said.

Go On

"I'm a pedalling fool and I'm heading for weather."
The weather came and he kept on going, right into
Winter, and the wind out of the north and no let-up–
We lived on a hill, and wind was what we got a lot of.

Then a night came along, and a blizzard was making,
Windows rattling and the whole house shaking,
But the iron man just hummed with the blast,
Said, "Come on, wind, and come on fast,
Show me your winter, make it nice and cool,
Show me your weather–I'm a pedalling fool!"
Gears all spinning, joints all shivering,
Sheet-iron clattering, cast-iron quivering till WHOMP!
The humming stopped, and we all sat up in bed with
Nothing to listen to but the wind right through into morning.

And there he was when we dug him out, propeller all bent.
One eye in the snow, and one eye
Staring up at the sky, still looking for weather.
He never let on he was beat, not him.

Well, my father put him on the roof again, this time
Without the propeller.
"Let him ride easy," he said. "A man can only take
Just so much north wind, even if he's iron."

1. The "pedalling man" in this poem is

   A. a delivery man.

   B. a man in a picture.

   C. a weathervane.

   D. a character in a radio series the speaker listened to.

2. What does the pedalling man NOT have?

A. a face

B. a bicycle

C. a purpose

D. flesh and blood

3. In the phrase, "a blizzard was *making*," the word *making* means

A. starting, getting under way.

B. coming from all directions at once.

C. destroying property.

D. ending, dying down.

4. What happens in the following lines?

The humming stopped, and we all sat up in bed with
Nothing to listen to but the wind right through into morning.

A. The pedalling man dies.

B. The blizzard drowns out the sound of the pedalling man.

C. The pedalling man falls off the roof.

D. The pedalling man refuses to pedal any longer.

5. Which literary element is most important in this poem?

A. Rhyme, because many of the lines end with a rhyme

B. Personification, because a nonhuman thing is described as if it were human

C. Rhythm, because there is a steady, regular beat, or meter

D. Simile, because there are many clever similes throughout the poem

How to Write a Short Response

What's Expected on the Test

In the last group of lessons, you learned how to answer multiple-choice questins. Now you will learn how to answer another type of question that is asked on the Ohio Proficiency Test: the short-answer question.

In a short-answer response, you write an answer of your own rather than choosing from four possible answers that are supplied to you. Your answer will probably be one or two sentences long. You should plan it carefully before you write. In planning, reread the poem at least once to make sure you understand it. Rereading will also help you find details for your answer.

Test-Taking Strategies

Read the Question Carefully

When you're taking a test under the pressure of time, it's easy to misread a question. Take the extra moment to make sure you understand all the words of the question and of the directions. You might underline key words in the question as an aid.

Be Complete

Some questions ask you to say more than one thing. Make sure you answer each part of the question. Give details whenever possible.

Be Clear

Write in complete sentences, in your clearest style. State your meaning; don't make the scorer guess at what you intend. Make sure all your facts are correct.

Be Accurate

Spell all names of characters and places correctly. If you mention a date or time, make sure you get it right. Check details by going back to the poem.

Reread Your Answer

Make sure you really wrote what you planned to write and didn't misstate yourself. Again, it's easy to feel rushed when you're taking a test. Don't breeze through, making careless errors.

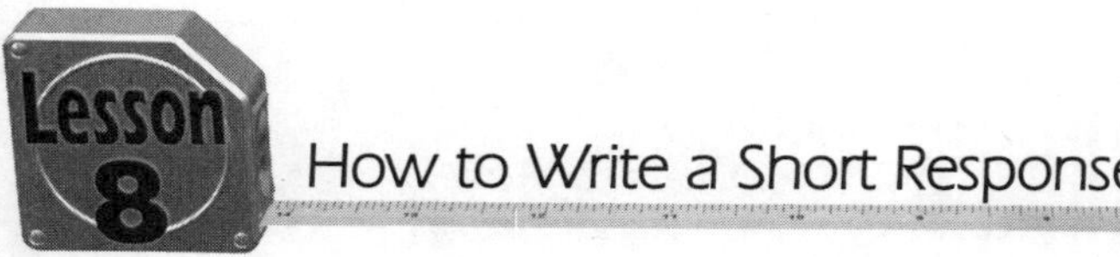

How to Write a Short Response

READING GUIDE

Directions Read the following and write your response on the lines provided.

The Grass
—by Emily Dickinson

1 The Grass so little has to do—
A Sphere of simple Green—
With only Butterflies to brood
2 And Bees to entertain—

And stir all day to pretty Tunes
3 The Breezes fetch along—
4 And hold the Sunshine in its lap
5 And bow to everything—

6 And thread the Dews all night, like Pearls—
And make itself so fine
A Duchess were[1] too common
7 For such a noticing—

And even when it dies—to pass
8 In Odors so divine—
Like Lowly spices, lain to sleep—
Or Spikenards,[2] perishing—

And then, in Sovereign Barns to dwell—
And dream the Days away,
The Grass so little has to do
9 I wish I were a Hay—

[1]**were:** would be
[2]**Spikenards:** a pleasantly smelling plant

GUIDED QUESTIONS

1. **Make a Prediction:** What is the "little" that the grass has to do?
2. **Link Ideas to Your Own Experience and Knowledge:** Based on your knowledge, what is Dickinson saying about grass?
3. **Form pictures:** What do you see based on this description?
4. What does the **figurative language** mean?
5. **Make an inference:** How can grass bow? (Also, what kind of **figurative language** is used in that description?)
6. **Check Your Understanding:** What does "thread the dews all night, like pearls" mean? Try to visualize the image in order to understand it.
7. What **comparison** or **contrast** is Dickinson making between the grass and a duchess?
8. **Connect Important Ideas:** How is dying grass like grass that's alive and green?
9. **Summarize:** Pack the meaning of the poem into a couple of sentences of prose.

Go on to the next page

READING GUIDE

10 What is Emily Dickinson's big idea about grass in this poem? Explain.

____

____

____

____

____

GUIDED QUESTIONS

10 **Make a Prediction:** Notice that this question asks you to identify the theme.

Directions Write your answer to the short-response question on the lines provided above.

Self-Evaluation

Ask yourself:

- Is my answer complete and appropriate?
- Do I show a thorough understanding of the poem?
- Does my answer display logical reasoning and conclusions?
- Is my answer accurate, relevant, comprehensive, and detailed?

How Your Response Will Be Evaluated

Your short-answer response will be graded by teachers using a rubric. A rubric is a set of criteria for scoring an answer. Criteria are standards by which something is measured.

The grading scale for these short-answer questions is 0-2, with 2 as the highest score.

Short-Answer Rubric

Score	Criteria
2	• Is complete and appropriate • Demonstrates a thorough understanding of the reading selection • Indicates logical reasoning and conclusions • Is accurate, relevant, comprehensive, and detailed
1	• Is partially appropriate • Contains minor flaws in reasoning or neglects to address some aspect of the item or question • Is mostly accurate and relevant but lacks comprehensiveness • Demonstrates an incomplete understanding of the reading selection or demonstrates an inability to make coherent meaning from the text
0	• Shows no understanding of the item or student fails to respond to item

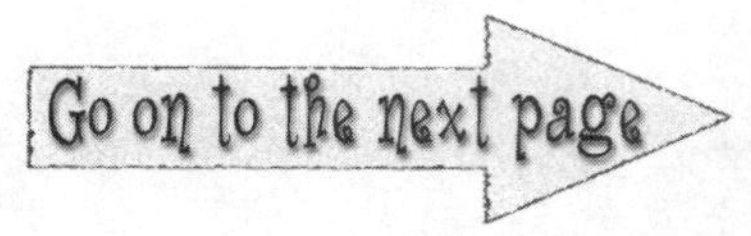

Lesson 9 How Your Response Will Be Evaluated

Question

What is Emily Dickinson's big idea about grass in this poem? Explain.

Sample Response

Her big idea is that the grass is beautiful because it is simple. Grass doesn't have to do anything; it just lies there, letting bees and butterflies fly over it, and allowing the breeze to play over it, and these things make it more beautiful than a duchess who devotes great care to making herself up.

Evaluation

This is a 2 response. It shows a thorough understanding of the poem. It answers the question comprehensively and in detail and it gives reasons that back up the student's point.

Activity

Directions Look again at your own answer. Using the rubric, write your evaluation of your answer on the lines below.

____

____

____

____

____

Recommend

What Is a Recommendation?

A recommendation of a poem is a statement saying whether you think other people would or would not like to read the poem. You have probably made recommendations of movies, TV shows, and CDs to friends and family members. When you say, "Yeah, go see that movie," you're recommending it.

But a well-planned recommendation must give a reason. "I think you should read this poem" is not a complete enough recommendation for the Ohio Proficiency Test! "I think you should read Dickinson's poem because it's about nature, which you like, and because the images in it are as beautiful as the grass they describe." Now *that's* a recommendation!

A recommendation may contain the phrase "I recommend" or "I do not recommend," but it doesn't have to.

Why Make a Recommendation?

One reason is because someone has asked you: "Should I see that movie or not?" Another reason is because you are so excited about something that you want to rush around sharing the news of it with people. (On the other hand, you might be so disgusted by something that you want to warn people away.)

Audience

Often, a particular work would be welcome to a particular person or persons. For example, the recommendation of Dickinson's poem was made to a particular reader who loves nature. Often, a work is appropriate for one age group but not another, or one interest group and not another.

Purpose

Your purposes are, basically, what you want to do and why. Your purposes affect your choices in life, including your reading choices. For example, if your cousin has just had a baby, you might recommend that she read a certain book on child-raising. Your cousin's purpose is to be the best mother possible, and your purpose is to help her. Together, these two purposes lead to your recommendation.

Go on to the next page

Activity

Directions Read the poem. Then write two different recommendations, based on the audiences and purposes shown. (Remember that your recommendation can be either positive or negative.) Then answer the questions that follow.

Monopoly

—by Alice Schertle

From the hilltop you can see
the city, like Monopoly,
laid out on a paper board.

Little pieces far below,
plastic houses row on row,
holding little plastic folk
asking how the game is scored.

Little unseen plastic folk
driving through the city smoke,
following the boulevards,
taking chances,
taking cards,
driving all across the board
asking how the game is scored.

Little busy businesses
laid out on the streets below,
waiting for the plastic folk
driving through the city smoke,
driving with little wheels,
moving forward, making deals:

Boardwalk,
Park Place,
Passing Go,
Reading Railroad,
B & O,
moving all across the board
asking how the game is scored.

Activity continued

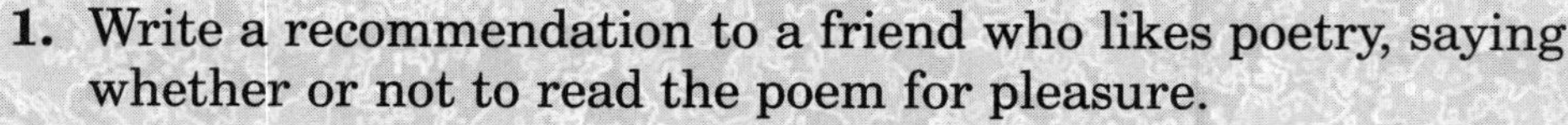

1. Write a recommendation to a friend who likes poetry, saying whether or not to read the poem for pleasure.

Kassy, I read a peom called Monopoly I think you should read it

2. Write a recommendation to the sixth-grade teachers in your school, saying whether or not you think the poem is a good one to assign in class.

Ms. Miller I do think it Should be assied becauce some I would enjoy

Go on to the next page

1. The poem would NOT be a good one to recommend to people who

   A. enjoy a combination of humor and seriousness.

   B. work in offices.

   C. have never played Monopoly.

   D. live in cities or suburbs.

2. Which of the following is NOT a possible purpose for reading the poem?

   A. to discover what a poet can do with the subject of Monopoly

   B. to learn what a poet thinks about life in present-day cities

   C. to appreciate songlike rhymes and rhythms

   D. to learn how to play Monopoly

3. Which of the following statements makes a negative recommendation?

   A. The poem makes us see modern city life in a new, unexpected way.

   B. The poem relies too much on one obvious, repeated comparison.

   C. The poem has a playful feel to it, but deeper down, it makes us think about some serious issues.

   D. This poem says things that I have thought, but it says them in a cleverer and more surprising way than I could.

Connect Content to Purpose

Purpose

Why Poets Write

When a writer sits down to write a poem, he or she probably wants to express feelings or ideas. The poet probably hopes you will be moved by the poem, too, and that's a kind of entertainment, very different from the kind of entertainment a comedian or a sports event provides. Most poems don't try to persuade or inform you, but that does happen sometimes. For instance, a patriotic poem may persuade people to fight in a war.

One Poem, Many Purposes

Of course, a poet can have more than one reason for writing a poem. And while writing it, the poet has to make a lot of decisions, and each of those has a reason, or purpose. For example, if the poet chooses to rhyme—or not to rhyme—it should be for a reason. Rhyme might sound too comic for some subjects, but it might be exactly right for lighter subjects.

How Content Supports Purpose

You, as a reader, can use the poem as a kind of trail that you can trace back to find the author's purposes. The way to do this is to keep asking yourself the question, "Why did the author do that instead of something else?" In a good poem, every word supports the poet's purpose. So you can ask, "Why did the poet do that?" about anything in the poem, from something big like, "Why did she choose this subject?" to something small like, "Why did he put the word *and* by itself on one line?"

Activity

Directions Read the poem, and then answer the questions.

Thomas Jefferson

—by Rosemary and Stephen Vincent Benet

Thomas Jefferson,
What do you say
Under the gravestone
Hidden away?

"I was a giver,
I was a molder,
I was a builder
With a strong shoulder."

Six feet and over,
Large-boned and ruddy,
The eyes grey-hazel
But bright with study.

The big hands clever
With pen and fiddle
And ready, ever,
For any riddle.

From buying empires
To planting 'taters,
From Declarations
to trick dumb-waiters.

"I liked the people,
The sweat and crowd of them,
Trusted them always
And spoke aloud of them.

"I liked all learning
And wished to share it
Abroad like pollen
For all who merit.

"I liked fine houses
With Greek pilasters,
And built them surely,
My touch a master's.

"I liked queer gadgets
And secret shelves,
And helping nations
To rule themselves.

"Jealous of others?
Not always candid?
But huge of vision
And open-handed.

"A wild-goose-chaser?
Now and again,
Build Monticello,
You little men!

"Design my plow, sirs,
they use it still,
Or found my college
At Charlottesville.

Activity continued

"And still go questing
New things and thinkers,
And keep as busy
As twenty thinkers.

"While always guarding
The people's freedom—
You need more hands, sir?
I didn't need 'em.

"They call you rascal?
They called me worse.
You'd do grand things, sir,
But lack the purse?

"I got no riches.
I died a debtor.
I died free-hearted
And that was better.

"For life was freakish
But life was fervent,
And I was always
Life's willing servant.

"Life, life's too weighty?
Too long a haul, sir?
I lived past eighty.
I liked it all, sir."

Go on to the next page

Activity continued

1. What do you think may have been the Benets' main purpose for writing this poem? Be specific.

   The main Purpose for writting this poem is to tell about Thomas Edison life and what he has been through

2. What may have been another specific purpose for writing this poem?

   Another purpose is for what events or anything else.

3. In the poem, Thomas Jefferson speaks from the grave. Why might the poets have chosen to present Jefferson that way, instead of, for example, just narrating Jefferson's life?

   The poet might have put him there because he is now dead and the poet felt made he could speak his life from his grave.

4. In the third and fourth stanzas, the poets describe Jefferson's physical size. Why do you think they devote part of their poem to that?

   Why they devote the part in the poem is because it is telling them his looks or personality.

5. The poets include some negative comments about Jefferson in the poem. For example, they say that he was jealous and not always honest. Why do you think they include negative comments?

   The poet includes it because he might of not been the best person in his time.

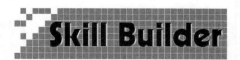

1. Which of the following shows that one purpose of the poem is to entertain?

   A. The poem is about Thomas Jefferson.

   B. The poem has a brisk, bouncy rhythm and clear, simple rhymes.

   C. The poem admits that Jefferson was jealous of others.

   D. The poem reminds us that Jefferson lived to be more than eighty years old.

2. Which of the following facts shows that one purpose of the poem is to persuade?

   A. The poem is divided into four-line stanzas.

   B. The poem gives many details about Jefferson's life.

   C. The poem was written by people who admired Jefferson.

   D. The poem praises Jefferson's greatness in phrases such as "guarding/The people's freedom" and "as busy/As twenty thinkers."

3. Which of the following shows that one purpose of the poem is to inform?

   A. The poem includes biographical facts many readers might not know already.

   B. The poem has Jefferson speak for himself with his words in quotation marks.

   C. The lines "For life was freakish/but life was fervent" are informational.

   D. The lines "Thomas Jefferson/What do you say" invite Jefferson to give his views.

4. State one possible purpose that you have thought of for the poem "Thomas Jefferson." In your opinion, is the poem successful in achieving that purpose, or not? Give a reason for your opinion.

____

____

____

____

____

Lesson 12 Vocabulary Development

Suffixes that Indicate Person

Some suffixes, or word endings, tell you that the word refers to a person doing something. For instance, in the poem "Thomas Jefferson," that great American says, "I was a giver,/ I was a molder,/ I was a builder. . . ." A giver is someone who gives; a molder is someone who molds; a builder is someone who builds. The *–er* suffix means "a person who."

***–Er* and Others**

–er may be the most common suffix indicating a person. Another spelling of it is *–or*. Jefferson says, "I died a debtor." A debtor is someone who has a debt or debts.

Jefferson also calls himself "Life's willing servant." That word uses the suffix *–ant*. A servant is someone who serves. A related suffix is *–ent*: Jefferson was president. A president is someone who presides, or has authority, over a nation.

And let's not forget three other person suffixes. Jefferson was a scientist, a politician, and an American. These words use the suffixes *–ist*, *–ian*, and *–an*. A scientist is someone who does science; a politician is someone who works in politics; and an American is someone from America.

Activity

A. **Directions** Fill in each blank with the appropriate word using a suffix indicating a person.

1. Someone who studies is called a ________________.
2. Someone who thinks is called a ________________.
3. Someone who does mathematics is called a ________________.
4. Someone who sails is called a ________________.
5. Someone who practices medicine is called a ________________.

Go on to the next page

Activity continued

B. **Directions** Guess the meaning of each boldfaced word. Look the words up afterward, if necessary.

1. For most of his life Jefferson was a **resident** of Virginia.

To be a citizen.

2. Jefferson was a keen **naturalist**, forever taking notes about the plant and animal life of his home state.

A scientist who studies nature.

3. Although not a professional architect, Jefferson was the **designer** of his own home, Monticello.

A person who build different types of

4. Jefferson was also the **inventor** of a new type of plow.

A person or scientist who makes something that

5. Jefferson did not excel as a public **speaker**.

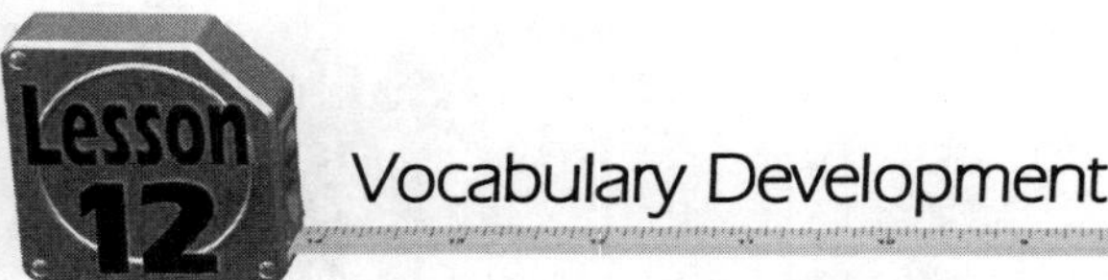

Vocabulary Development

1. Jefferson wrote most of the Declaration of Independence. Two words describing someone who writes something are
   - **A.** writer and auther.
   - **B.** writer and author.
   - **C.** auther and writor.
   - **D.** author and writor.

2. Jefferson belonged to the committee in charge of creating the Declaration. In other words, he was a ________ of that committee.
   - **A.** governor
   - **B.** supporter
   - **C.** member
   - **D.** signer

3. When Jefferson was president, the U.S. became the purchaser of the Louisiana territory. In other words, the U.S. ________ Louisiana.
   - **A.** defeated
   - **B.** settled
   - **C.** fought
   - **D.** bought

4. Discuss Thomas Jefferson on the lines below. Use at least three words containing suffixes indicating person. Write complete sentences. Underline the words containing the person suffixes.

____

____

____

____

Directions: Read the selection and answer the questions.

The Way through the Woods

By Rudyard Kipling

They shut the road through the woods
Seventy years ago.
Weather and rain have undone it again,
And now you would never know
There was once a road through the woods
Before they planted the trees.
It is underneath the coppice[1] and heath[2],
And the thin anemones[3].
Only the keeper sees
That, where the ring-dove broods,
And the badgers roll at ease,
There was once a road through the woods.

Yet, if you enter the woods
Of a summer evening late,
When the night-air cools on the trout-ringed pools
Where the otter whistles his mate
(They fear not men in the woods,
Because they see so few),
You will hear the beat of the horse's feet,
And the swish of a skirt in the dew,
Steadily cantering[4] through
The misty solitudes,
As though they perfectly knew
The old lost road through the woods . . . . . .
But there is no road through the woods.

[1]**coppice:** a small woods
[2]**heath:** open land containing many shrubs
[3]**anemones:** flowers of a buttercup type found in Britain
[4]**cantering:** riding at an easy gallop

1. Compared to what it was seventy years earlier, the road during the poet's time is

   A. the same.

   B. much busier.

   C. gone.

   D. broader.

2. Which of the following did NOT help cause the change in the road?

   A. Someone shut the road.

   B. People stopped traveling on the road.

   C. Weather affected the road.

   D. War destroyed the road.

3. Based on the text of the poem, what was probably Kipling's purpose in writing it?

   A. He wanted to entertain readers with beautiful descriptions.

   B. He wanted to advertise the road to travelers.

   C. He wanted to inform his fellow countrymen about poor highway management.

   D. He wanted to advertise the road to travelers.

4. To critique and evaluate this poem, which literary element would be most important?

   A. sensory imagery

   B. simile

   C. plot

   D. character

Go On

5. What is the overall mood or feeling of the poem?
   A. cheerful and sunny
   B. quietly haunted and dark
   C. angrily making fun of humanity
   D. dizzy with romantic love

6. Would you or would you not recommend this poem for sixth-grade classes? Explain why, referring to specific aspects of the text.

____

____

____

____

____

How to Write an Extended Response

What's Expected on the Test?

Another type of question found on the Ohio Proficiency Test is the extended-response question. Like a short-response question, an extended-response question asks you to think for yourself. It will probably ask you to support your ideas with details from the selection. An extended response is usually several sentences long, and it contains more detail than a short response.

An extended-response question may ask you to retell what is in the poem. This means that you should put the important contents of the poem into your own words.

You might also be asked for a personal response in this type of question. In a personal response, connect what you read to your own life and experience.

On the other hand, an extended-response question may ask you to write critically. This means that you should think about what is effective or not effective about the poem, and support your judgment with evidence.

Test-Taking Strategies

Read the Question Carefully

If you're pressed for time on a test, you might skip over words and misunderstand directions. For instance, you might misread *rhythm*s as *rhymes*. By being careful, you can avoid making this kind of mistake. Read each question at least twice. Ask yourself: What are they asking for?

Look for Key Words

Test questions often contain signal words, showing you what the question calls for. For example, if the question asks you to *compare* and *contrast*, that's a signal telling you to find ways in which two things are alike or unlike. If a question asks you to retell, that's a signal that you should put the poem's contents into your own words.

Stick to the Topic

When you write a long answer, it's easy to wander off course. Stay focused. Make sure that every part of your answer really answers the question.

Answer All Parts of the Question

In an extended response, you may need to do more than one thing. For example, a question may ask, "Where are personification and sensory images used in 'The Pedalling Man'?" If you just give examples of sensory images, and forget to mention examples of personification, you'll only get partial credit for the question. Ask yourself: Have I left anything out? Have I answered everything they asked?

Using Connecting Words and Phrases

Connecting words show your reader how each of your ideas is related to the ideas that come before it and after it. Use connecting words like *because*, *since*, *so*, *thus*, *first*, *second*, *next*, *last*, and *afterward* to make these relationships clear.

READING GUIDE

Directions Read the following poem. Use the questions at the right to help you use reading strategies. Plan an answer to the extended-response question. Write your answer on the lines provided.

Someone

—Walter de la Mare

Someone came knocking
1 At my wee, small door;
Someone came knocking,
2 I'm sure—sure—sure;
I listened, I opened,
3 I looked to left and right,
But nought[1] there was a-stirring[2]
4 In the still, dark night;
Only the busy beetle
Tap-tapping in the wall,
Only from the forest
The screech owl's call,
Only the cricket whistling
5 While the dewdrops fall,
6 So I know not who came knocking,
7 At all, at all, at all.

[1]**nought:** nothing.
[2]**a-stirring:** moving.

GUIDED QUESTIONS

1 Make an **inference:** Who is speaking, and where is he or she?

2 **Link this idea to your own experience and knowledge:** If you repeated, "I'm sure," in this situation, how sure would you really be?

3 What do these lines make you see and hear? **Form a picture of the scene.**

4 What do you **predict** will happen—who or what caused the noise?

5 Are the beetle, the owl, and the cricket the kinds of things the speaker was listening for? **Compare and contrast** the speaker's ideas with reality.

6 **Confirm and revise** your earlier **prediction:** Did what you expected happen?

7 **Summarize** the poem: What's it about, where does it take place, and what happens in it?

Go on to the next page

READING GUIDE

8 **Sample Extended-Response Question**

What do you think the speaker of the poem heard? What do you think he *thought* he heard? Support your response with reasons based on the poem and on your own knowledge.

____

____

____

____

____

____

____

____

____

____

GUIDED QUESTIONS

8 **Notice that this question asks you to compare and contrast what you think the speaker heard with what the speaker thought he heard. Are these two things the same or different?**

Activity

Directions Write your answer to the extended-response question on the lines provided under the question.

Self-Evaluation

Ask yourself:

- Is my answer detailed and well-elaborated with evidence?
- Is my answer well-organized?
- Does my answer show logical reasoning based on the poem and on my knowledge?
- Does my answer address all the parts of the question, and not go off course?

How Your Response Will Be Evaluated

Your answer will be evaluated on a scale of 0-4, with 4 as the highest score. Teachers will use the rubric below to grade your answer. Study the rubric so that as you take the Ohio Proficiency Test, you will be able to evaluate and improve your answers.

Extended-Response Rubric

Score	Criteria
4	• Provides extensive evidence of the kind of interpretation called for in the item or question • Is well organized, elaborate, and thorough • Demonstrates a complete understanding of the whole work as well as how the parts blend to form the whole • Is relevant, comprehensive, and detailed, demonstrating a thorough understanding of the reading selection • Addresses thoroughly the important elements of the question • Contains logical reasoning and communicates effectively and clearly *(A four-point response may go beyond the requirements of the item.)*
3	• Provides evidence that essential interpretation has been made • Is thoughtful and reasonably accurate • Indicates an understanding of the concept or item • Communicates adequately, and generally reaches reasonable conclusions • Contains some combination of the following flaws: ◆ Minor flaws in reasoning or interpretation ◆ Failure to address some aspect of the item or omission of some detail
2	• Is mostly accurate and relevant • Contains some combination of the following flaws: ◆ Incomplete evidence of interpretation ◆ Unsubstantiated statements made about the text ◆ Incomplete understanding of the concept or item ◆ Lack of comprehensiveness, faulty reasoning, unclear communication

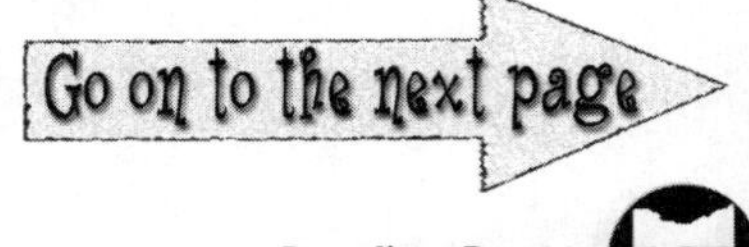

1	● Provides little evidence of interpretation ● Is unorganized and incomplete ● Exhibits decoding rather than reading ● Indicates some effort beyond restating the item ● Contains some combination of the following flaws: ◆ Little understanding of the concept or item ◆ Failure to address most aspects of the item ◆ Inability to make coherent meaning from the text

0	● Shows no understanding of the item or student fails to respond to item

Question

What do you think the speaker of the poem heard? What do you think he thought he heard? Support your response with reasons based on the poem and on your own knowledge.

Sample Response

The speaker is living in a woods, or at least some place where owls and crickets and beetles are nearby, and he (it might be a she but I'm calling it "he" because the poet is male) has a "wee, small door," which might mean that he's a poor person in a small cottage, or even that he's a leprechaun or elf. He might be a child or an adult. I think he's a child because he hears a little sound and it startles him. That happens to kids a lot, and usually it turns out to be nothing, or the house settling, or something like that. It's possible that that's all that happens in this poem, too. But it's possible that something creepy does knock at his door but disappears. The fact that it can't be proven makes the poem spooky and fun. We can't tell whether what he thought happened really happened or not.

Evaluation

This response gets a score of 4. It answers both parts of the question, shows the way the parts are related, and shows that the student understands and has thought about what goes on in the poem. It is well organized, leading from facts to interpretations.

Activity

Directions Exchange your extended response with a classmate. Evaluate each other's response, using the rubric. Write your evaluation on the lines below.

____

____

____

____

____

Proofreading Practice

Proofreading means rereading your work carefully one final time, to correct any mistakes. Always proofread your extended responses. Look for errors in:

- grammar
- spelling
- capitalization
- punctuation

Activity

Directions The paragraph below contains ten errors. Proofread the passage and correct all the errors.

Someone is the titel of a poem about someone knocking at a door. The door to someones house in the forest. The guy who's speaking says that a knock woke him up at night, the speaker looked "to left and right," but didn't see anything. Could it have been a cricket or a beetle or an owl. At the end of the poem, the guy still doesnt know what hapened. I think he herd a ghost. I just get the feeling.

Independent Practice for the Test

Directions: Read the selection and answer the questions.

How to Tell the Wild Animals
by Carolyn Wells

If ever you should go by chance
To jungles in the East;
And if there should to you advance
A large and tawny beast,
If he roars at you as you're dyin'
You'll know it is the Asian lion.

Or if sometime when roaming round,
A noble wild beast greets you,
With black stripes on a yellow ground,
Just notice if he eats you.
This simple rule may help you learn
The Bengal Tiger to discern.

If strolling forth, a beast you view,
Whose hide with spots is peppered,
As soon as he has lept on you,
You'll know it is the Leopard.
'Twill do no good to roar with pain,
He'll only lep and lep again.

If when you're walking 'round your yard,
You meet a creature there,
Who hugs you very, very hard,
Be sure it is the Bear.
If you have any doubt, I guess
He'll give you just one more caress.

Though to distinguish beasts of prey
A novice might nonplus,
The Crocodiles you always may
Tell from Hyenas thus:
Hyenas come with merry smiles;
But if they weep, they're Crocodiles.

Go On

The true Chameleon is small,
A lizard sort of thing;
He hasn't any ears at all,
And not a single wing.
If there is nothing on the tree,
'Tis the Chameleon you see.

1. This poem tells how to

A. escape from the jungle.

B. hunt large animals.

C. recognize beasts of prey.

D. trap hyenas and other animals by using trickery.

2. What is the tone of the poem?

A. humorous

B. serious

C. terrifying

D. stern

3. In line 5, why does the poet write *dyin'* instead of *dying*?

A. She does not know the correct spelling.

B. She is making fun of her character's speech.

C. *Dyin'* rhymes with *lion.*

D. Nobody really pronounces the final *g.*

4. Which word in the poem was made up by the poet?

A. Bengal

B. 'Tis

C. discern

D. lep

5. How is the last stanza of the poem different from all the other stanzas?

   A. It is about an animal that isn't dangerous.

   B. It has fewer lines than the other stanzas.

   C. It doesn't have as many rhymes.

   D. It sums up the other stanzas.

6. In your own words, state the meaning of the lines, "Though to distinguish beasts of prey/A novice might nonplus,/The Crocodiles you always may/Tell from Hyenas thus:"

   These lines mean that you can always tell the difference between a crocodile and a hyenas

7. In a paragraph, retell the contents of the poem.

Workshop

Choose Materials

1. Go to the school library or public library and find the section of poetry books for young people. Some of the books will be collections of poems by one person. Others will be collections by many authors in one volume. The latter are called anthologies. Find five or more poems that express hope or joy and five that express sorrow or despair. Try to include at least one author who has written poems of both types. On the lines below, write the titles and authors of all the poems you selected.

Poems of Hope and Joy	Poems of Sorrow and Despair

2. Below are ten topics. Choose one topic and search for poems about it. Jot down the names of at least five poems that you find on the topic. Read two of those poems. Jot down your responses to each poem. Pick another topic and repeat the process. You may wish to share responses with your class.

work	the teenage years	love
childhood	parenthood	play
war	education	nature
the universe		

Home Involvement Activities

Speaking and Listening Activity

Give a poetry reading in your class, or in your home, or at a civic group, or for a group of friends. Choose approximately six to eight poems that move you or impress you. Practice reading them aloud with appropriate expression, in a natural tone of voice. Then gather your audience and read to them. It would be fun to have several readers, each choosing his or her own favorite poems. You might want to save time for a discussion period after the reading. Even if there isn't a formal discussion period, some people will probably want to hang around and talk about the poems anyway!

Reading Activity

Become the editor of your own poetry anthology. Choose your favorite poems, and put them in a folder or staple them together. Include at least a dozen poems and no more than fifty. You might want to limit your selection to poems on a specific subject, such as youth, or to poets of a specific type, such as American poets of the twentieth and twenty-first centuries. Decide on a title that reflects your subject or your tastes. Arrange the poems in a suitable order, perhaps by the poet's date of birth or by each poem's date of publication, or perhaps by subject or theme. On the cover, include the title of the anthology, your name as editor, and a picture or design. If you wish, illustrate some or all of the poems. Also, write an introduction discussing the poems. Comment on what unifies the poems as a group. Discuss some of the poems individually; but you don't have to mention every poem. Don't forget to put a table of contents at the beginning of the book. At the end of the book, supply a list of contributors (that is, of poets in the anthology). Give a bit of information about each poet. For example, you might include each poet's date and place of birth, date of death (if applicable), the place where the poet lived, how the poet made his or her living, and the titles of the poet's most important works.

Share your anthology with people you know who like poetry. Bear in mind that most of the poems will probably be copyrighted by their authors. So you can't sell your anthology; it's just for your own private use.

Invasion of the Poets

With a group or by yourself, create a dramatic presentation in which you play the roles of your favorite poets. Read enough poems so that you feel really familiar with the poets' work. Find and read biographies or biographical articles about the poets. For classic poets such as Emily Dickinson or Robert Frost, that will be easy; for present-day poets, ask a librarian to help you. Articles about many present-day authors can be found in the reference book series *Something About the Author* and *Contemporary Authors.*

Once you've become an expert, stage an "invasion" of your class by the poets. These poets are tired of being ignored; they want to tell about themselves. They want to read their work to a captive audience. This is the creative part of the activity, and how you do it is your own decision. You choose which parts of the poets' lives and work to highlight. You choose whether or not to use costumes and props and illustrations, and if so, which ones. You choose what medium to use—live or tape, dramatic skit or panel discussion, or multimedia, or something completely different. Have fun!

Chapter 3 Reading Nonfiction

What's Coming Up?

In this chapter, you will learn:

- what nonfiction is
- how to read nonfiction
- how to answer multiple-choice questions
- how to analyze words
- how to compare and contrast
- how to analyze cause and effect
- how to differentiate fact and opinion
- how to summarize
- how to make inferences
- how to critique and evaluate organizational structure
- how to critique and evaluate logical reasoning
- how to make a recommendation
- how to connect content to purpose

Does This Sound Familiar?

- During an after-school basketball game at a community center, the two coaches disagree about the referee's call. The referee pulls out a copy of the rule book and reads the rule aloud to both teams.
- You receive a computer for your birthday. To set it up, you and your parents consult the printed manual and the onscreen Read Me document.
- You're at a restaurant, deciding what to order. You read the delicious-sounding names and descriptions of all the dishes on the menu.
- A magazine cover appeals to you in the supermarket. You take the magazine home and read a profile of your favorite star.
- You can't get to sleep at night. You open a history of ancient Rome. That'll do the trick, you think. But, surprise—you stay awake reading it.

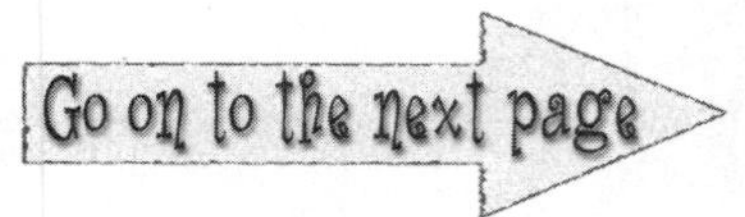

Chapter 3 Reading Nonfiction

Nonfiction Is All Around You

If you go to a library or bookstore, you'll find that most of the books there are not novels or poetry or plays—they're nonfiction. Many people love to read stories for entertainment, but almost everybody, at some point, finds there's something they *must* read—to learn a fact, to learn how to do something, to keep up with the world, or to guide their own lives. Would you like to learn how child labor was ended in the United States in the early 1900s? Read *Kids on Strike!* by Susan Campbell Bartoletti. Would you like to be inspired by the life of a great photographer who traveled around the world? Try *Margaret Bourke-White: Her Pictures Were Her Life*, by Susan Goldman Rubin. Are you interested in the history behind the legend of King Arthur? A good choice for you might be *The World of King Arthur and His Court* by Kevin Crossley-Holland. Would you like to know how famous writers remember their growing-up years? Then the books for you are the two volumes of *When I Was Your Age, Original Stories About Growing Up*, edited by Amy Ehrlich.

Activity

Directions Work with a partner. Fill out the chart below. Under each category, list at least five opportunities. Then share your findings with your classmates.

Reading	Performing	Listening	Viewing
book	Plays	radio	book
			TV

Lesson 1 What Is Nonfiction?

Nonfiction contains information about real-life people, places, events, and things. If you read a book about how to use the Internet, you are reading nonfiction. If you read an article about the life of Julius Caesar, you are reading nonfiction. If you see a documentary about bears in the wild, you are watching nonfiction. If you hear a news story about the next election, you are hearing nonfiction.

While fiction is made-up, nonfiction is just the opposite. It contains actual facts, data, and statistics about the real world.

Forms of Nonfiction

Print	Non-print	Electronic Media
history book	newscast	CD-ROM encyclopedia
newspaper	documentary	e-mail message
atlas	televised biography	Web site
brochure	talk show	laser disc
pamphlet	interview	on-line dictionary

Special Text Features

The purpose of nonfiction is to provide information. It has certain features that organize this information and help you understand it more easily.

Subheads Information is often chunked, or divided up into sections. When this occurs, subheads often provide a title for each section. These subheads tell you what the section is about.

Sidebars Sometimes nonfiction provides extra information in sidebars, or text put to the side of the article. These sidebars are often interesting, but they are not essential to understanding the article.

Special vocabulary Nonfiction often contains special vocabulary—words that are used in a specific subject in a specific way. These words may be defined for you. There may even be a vocabulary box in the article.

Graphic aids Information can be presented in graphic form. These forms include charts, graphs, diagrams, maps, and illustrations. All of them help you picture the information.

Captions Captions tell you about the graphic aids. They clarify what you are seeing. Captions may appear under the graphic or to the side of it.

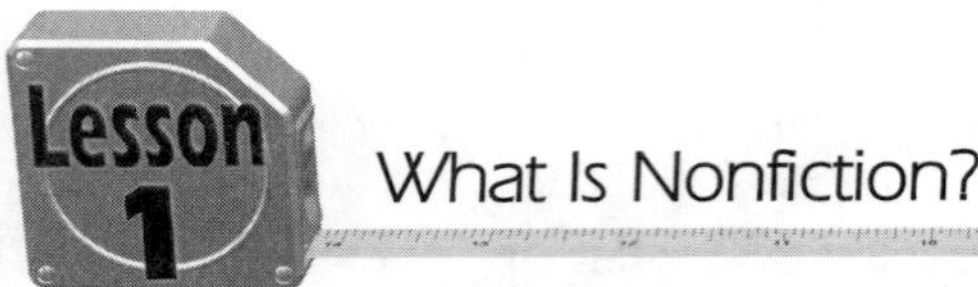

Lesson 1 What Is Nonfiction?

Purpose

When you read for information, you may want to:

- **find** specific facts or data
- **understand** a subject more thoroughly
- **solve** problems
- **figure out** how to do something
- simply **enjoy** what you are reading

Rate

Your rate of reading refers to how quickly or slowly you read something. Your rate is connected to your purpose and to how difficult the material is.

- **Read slowly and carefully** when you:
  - study for a test
  - want to learn about a difficult subject
  - see a lot of hard words
  - need to take time to think about ideas
- **Skim**, or glance through the article without reading every word, when you:
  - just want to get a general idea of what the subject is about
  - can't decide whether or not you want to read the article
- **Scan**, or let your eyes search for specific information, when you:
  - want to find specific information
  - are looking for the answer to a question
  - are searching for names and dates
- **Read at a comfortable rate** when you:
  - are reading for enjoyment
  - think the information is easy

Activity

Directions Read each situation below. Explain what your purpose for reading and your reading rate would be.

1. You just got a new 12-speed bicycle. It comes with a manual telling you how to shift gears.

   Purpose figure out Rate slowly

2. You are really interested in Egyptian mummies. You see an article in a magazine.

   Purpose enjoy Rate slowly

3. At the bookstore, you see a book about gardening. You wonder if it contains the information you need about growing tomatoes.

   Purpose find Rate scan

4. You are writing a report on the Chippewa Indians. You want to locate the names of three of their chiefs.

   Purpose find Rate skim

5. You are studying the life cycle of the butterfly. The book you are reading has quite a few words you don't know. The concepts are a little difficult to understand.

   Purpose understand Rate carefully

Lesson 2 How to Read Nonfiction

How do you become a better reader of nonfiction? What strategies and skills will help you get the most meaning out of what you read? Read the Keys to Success below for tips on how to be a successful reader.

Keys To Success

APPLY READING STRATEGIES

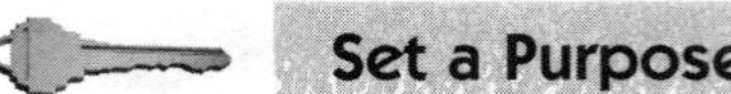

Set a Purpose

Your purpose is your reason for reading. It is why you are trying to find out the things you are trying to find out. Before you begin reading, set a purpose. Read to carry out this purpose.

Make, Confirm, and Revise Predictions

You have done this already when reading fiction and poetry. In reading nonfiction, it is even more important to update and correct your predictions when you learn new facts and details. After all, these predictions refer to the real world, not to a made-up story.

Retell

Often, nonfiction material becomes easier to grasp if you can retell it to yourself as a story or narrative. Try it!

Connect Important Ideas

How does Fact A make Detail B more believable? How does one expert's opinion support or overturn another's? How does an idea that seemed vague at first seem clearer at last? A nonfiction article is made up of facts, reasons, and ideas. Look for how one building block supports another.

Link Ideas to Your Own Experience and Knowledge

You may already know something about your topic. Imagine your prior knowledge as a reference book. Keep it open and ready to flip through in your mind. Based on what you already know, you might question the author's statements. Alternatively, based on what you read, you might question what you thought you already knew.

Use Graphic Devices

The kinds of graphic devices you might find in nonfiction include charts, tables, graphs, diagrams, maps, lists, pictures with captions, timelines, and more. Online nonfiction sources may include hyperlinks and video clips. Use these visual aids as footholds to help you achieve your understanding of the text.

Form Pictures

This is related to "Retell." Both skills can give life to dry data. If you are reading about ancient Egypt, for example, try to see the pyramids, the pharaohs, the Nile river, the mummies, in your mind. You will become more interested in the material, and you will probably understand it better.

Check Your Understanding

You may have used a reading strategy correctly but come up with an incorrect view. For example, when you visualized a mummy, you may have imagined something more like a creature from a movie than like a real mummified corpse. Check your accuracy. Look for pictures of things you have visualized. Look up hard words in the dictionary. Reread confusing passages to clear them up. Ask yourself questions, and read ahead to find the answers. Look for additional sources to support, correct, or balance your main source.

Analyze Word Origins

Nonfiction often contains difficult words. Looking a new word up in the dictionary is, of course, the best way to learn its meaning. In addition to the definition, look at the part of the dictionary entry that gives the word's origin. This can increase your understanding of the word.

Go on to the next page

LOOK FOR ELEMENTS OF NONFICTION

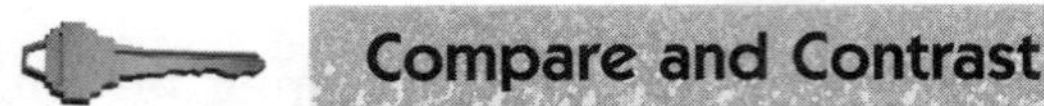

Compare and Contrast

When you compare two things, you show how they are alike. When you contrast two things, you show how they are different. When you read, analyze the text and look for comparisons and contrasts.

Analyze Cause and Effect

A cause is what makes something happen. It is the reason behind an action. An effect is what happens. It is the result of the cause. When you read, analyze the text and look for causes and effects.

Distinguish Fact and Opinion

A fact is something that can be proved. An opinion is a personal belief or judgment. It cannot be proved. When you read, analyze the text and look for facts and opinions.

Summarize

A summary provides the main points of what you read in a concise form. Because it focuses only on what is important, it leaves out extra details. When you read, pause from time to time to summarize.

Make Inferences

An inference is an educated guess you make after looking at the details and reading between the lines. You use evidence from the text to grasp an idea not stated directly in the text. When you read nonfiction, you use facts, statistics, examples, anecdotes, and your own knowledge and experience as the basis for your inferences.

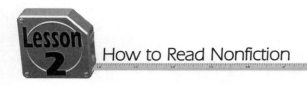

Critique and Evaluate Organization

When you critique and evaluate a work of nonfiction, you discuss its strengths and weaknesses. You state your opinion of how effective the author's choices were. You give your reasons. In critiquing and evaluating organization, first ask: What form of organization did the author choose? Then you ask: Did that form of organization make the work more effective, or less effective? Give reasons.

Critique and Evaluate Logical Reasoning

Does the author appeal to logic or to emotion? Does some of the evidence conflict with other evidence? Is there too little evidence? Is some of the evidence biased or out-of-date? If the evidence is sound, has the author jumped to conclusions from it? These are some basic questions to ask in evaluating logical reasoning. Make sure you yourself have reasons for your answers to these questions.

Connect Content to Purpose

A nonfiction author might be writing with the purpose of persuading you, or entertaining you, or informing you, or expressing a personal feeling. Examine the kinds of evidence and argument the author includes. Examine the kinds of words the author uses. Think about how these choices by the author support the author's specific purpose.

The article you are going to read is about one of the pharaohs in ancient Egypt—a woman named Hatshepsut. Here are some facts you should know about ancient Egypt before you start reading.

- The ancient Egyptian civilization began over 5,000 years ago. It lasted over 3,000 years.
- The civilization grew up along the Nile Valley.
- The ruler was called the pharaoh (**fair**-oh).
- The pharaohs built elaborate tombs for their burials. The best-known tombs are the pyramids.

READING GUIDE

Directions Put your key strategies to work as you read the article. Look for the elements of literature, too. Refer to the questions on the side.

The Woman Pharaoh
—Jena Malone

The greatest queen in the history of ancient Egypt was . . . ?

1 We understand why you probably answered Cleopatra to the question above. The woman who charmed Julius Caesar and Mark Anthony, the most powerful men of ancient Rome, has always been considered the most famous Egyptian queen. But, guess what? She wasn't the greatest.

What if we told you there was a woman more
2 impressive than Cleopatra; someone who dressed like a man, married her half-brother, built some of her civilization's most interesting structures, and was one of the most successful pharaohs in Egypt's history. Her name? Hatshepsut.

Nearly 150 years ago, archaeologists discovered the grand temple of this fascinating female pharaoh who ruled Egypt almost 3,500 years ago. Through careful reading of
3 the hieroglyphs[1] in her temple and analysis of other artifacts[2] from her time, scholars have a pretty good idea of

[1]**hieroglyph** (hī′ər ō glif) n.: a picture or symbol representing an object, letter, or sound.
[2]**artifacts** (ärt′ə faktz) n.: objects made by human beings.

GUIDED QUESTIONS

1 **Link Ideas to Your Own Experience and Knowledge.** Had you ever heard of Cleopatra before reading this article? Had you heard of Hatshepsut?

2 **Differentiate Fact and Opinion** Is it fact or opinion to rank Hatshepsut above Cleopatra? Explain.

3 **Vocabulary/Word Origins** What is the meaning of the words *hieroglyphs* and *artifacts*? Use the footnotes to help you. Use a dictionary to find their origins.

READING GUIDE

what Hatshepsut's life might have been like and what she
4 accomplished during her reign. Here is her story.

5 The Future Queen

Hatshepsut was the beautiful eldest daughter of the highly respected pharaoh, Tuthmosis I, and his queen, Ahmose. It was uncommon for Egyptian girls to be educated, but Tuthmosis I wanted Hatshepsut to be schooled by the royal scribe. Her education would come in handy since both of her brothers died young, leaving no male heir to Egypt's throne.

After her father's death, Hatshepsut's 12-year-old half-brother, Tuthmosis II, was crowned pharaoh. To strengthen his position, and in keeping with Egyptian
6 tradition, he married his 14-year-old half-sister.
Hatshepsut was now Queen of Egypt. During her rule, she commissioned Senemut, her boyfriend and a member of her royal court, to build her a grand burial temple at Thebes in the Valley of the Kings. Named "Splendor of
7 Splendor," the temple was built into a large cliff and was
dedicated to the gods Amon and Hathor. About 150 years ago, archaeologists discovered the temple buried under hundreds of tons of sand. A monastery had been resting on the site and that's how the temple came to be known as
8 "Deir el Bahari" (**Dare**-l-Bahri), which is Arabic for
"Northern Monastery."

Hatshepsut believed she was of divine birth, like a god. And this charismatic leader wasn't shy about honoring herself and her achievements. Her image adorned huge sphinxes on the temple's ground level, and along its upper terrace, her smiling face was carved into statues.

Tales of Hatshepsut's reign over Egypt were inscribed in hieroglyphs, and illustrations on the temple's walls. Her late father's architect, Ineni, was commissioned to build a secret burial chamber to house her mummy and other precious goods that she would take with her to the afterlife. One legend says that the tomb was built by 100
9 slaves who were later killed to protect its secret location.

Egypt's Female Pharaoh

With Hatshepsut as Queen, Tuthmosis II ruled Egypt for about 14 years. Before he died, Tuthmosis II decreed

GUIDED QUESTIONS

4 **Connect Content to Purpose** What do you think are the author's purposes for writing this article? How can you tell, based on the article's content and the way it is written?

5 **Text Features** Use the subtitle. What will this section be about?

6 **Analyze Cause and Effect** Why did Tuthmosis marry his half-sister?

7 **Form Pictures** Visualize the "Splendor of Splendors." Describe what you see.

8 **Vocabulary/Text Features** How do you pronounce Deir el Bahari? What does it mean?

9 **Retell** Imagine yourself telling an adult the story of Hatshepsut. What would you say so far?

Go on to the next page

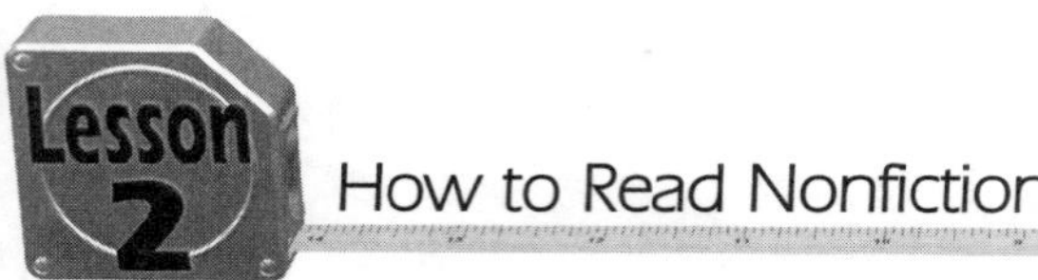

READING GUIDE

that his young son, Tuthmosis III, would be crowned the next pharaoh. But Tuthmosis III was too young to rule Egypt alone. Hatshepsut crowned herself co-pharaoh until
10 Tuthmosis III grew up.

DIG DATA: During the time of the pharaohs, Egyptian women had more freedom and legal rights than women in societies such as Greece. Egyptian women could own property, hold official positions, and inherit land from
11 their parents.

In 1473 B.C., Hatshepsut became the ruler of Egypt. As pharaoh, she dressed as a male pharaoh would dress, complete with the shendyt, or kilt, headdress, and fake beard. When she traveled to other countries, she posed as a man so that she and Egypt would be treated with respect.

During her rule as pharaoh, Hatshepsut built more monuments and works of art than any other queen in Egypt's history, including two gigantic red granite obelisks constructed for the Temple of Karnuk in Thebes. She also expanded Egypt's territory and trade with neighboring countries. Her most successful trade relationship was
12 known as the Expedition to Punt, modern-day Somalia. In 1493 B.C., she sent a fleet of five ships on the trading expedition. They returned with gold, spices like frankincense and myrrh, fragrant oils (used for religious ceremonies), monkeys, wood, ebony, ivory, and ointments to make cosmetics. The details of the Punt expedition were inscribed on the walls of Hatshepsut's grand temple.

13 Her Mysterious Death

Hatshepsut ruled for more than 20 years until Tuthmosis III was old enough to claim his birthright. There are two theories about what became of her next. Some archaeologists think Tuthmosis III was jealous of Hatshepsut's power, so he had her killed. Other scholars say that she peacefully passed her crown to Tuthmosis III. We do know that after Hatshepsut's death, later rulers destroyed hieroglyphs and statues to erase any record of
14 her reign.

GUIDED QUESTIONS

10 **Cause and Effect** Why did Hatshepsut crown herself co-pharaoh?

11 **Comparison and Contrast** How was life different for women in ancient Egypt and women in ancient Greece?

12 **Check Your Understanding** Why was Hatshepsut considered a great queen?

13 **Text Features** What will this section be about?

14 **Make Inferences** Why do you think later rulers erased records of her reign?

READING GUIDE

We also know that Hatshepsut's secret burial temple was discovered and destroyed and her mummy was stolen. The only remaining artifact from her burial tomb was a canopic jar with her liver inside. (A canopic jar was a container which held the internal organs of mummies.) So Hatshepsut's death may be more of a mystery than her life. Perhaps some day archaeologists will find the evidence that will unravel the mystery and reveal the complete story
15 of Egypt's greatest woman ruler.

16 **Hatshep-Sphinx**
In ancient Egypt, it was common for pharaohs to be depicted as stone sphinxes. This statue of Hatshepsut can be seen at New York City's Metropolitan Museum.

17, 18, 19

GUIDED QUESTIONS

15 **Summarize** Summarize the information in this section.

16 **Text Features** What information do you learn from the caption?

17 **Connect Important Ideas** How do people today learn new things about life in ancient Egypt? Find several places in the article that point this out.

18 **Critique and Evaluate Organizational Structure** Does the article flow clearly from point to point? Explain any cases in which your answer is "No."

19 **Critique and Evaluate Logical Reasoning** Does the article give convincing evidence that Hatshepsut was greater than Cleopatra? Why or why not? If you are unconvinced, what more would you need to convince you?

Fluency Tip

The names of ancient Egyptians were long, and to us, a little difficult to pronounce. Here's a trick to help you read smoothly. The first time you read the article, use a letter in place of the name. This means that Hatshepsut becomes H and Tuthmosis becomes T.

The second time you read the article, break the names into syllables. This will help you pronounce them.

Hatshepsut	Hat shep sut
Tuthmosis	Tuth mo sis
Senemut	Se ne mut

Lesson 3 How to Answer Multiple-Choice Questions

What's Expected on the Test?

One or more of the reading selections on the Ohio Proficiency Test will probably be nonfiction. Some of the questions you will be asked about the nonfiction will be multiple-choice. In this lesson you will learn some helpful strategies for dealing with those questions.

Test-Taking Strategies

First, Read All the Questions

After reading the passage, read all the questions, one after another, before you answer any of them. This gives you two advantages. First, it gives you time to think. Second, it gives you an overview, a general idea, of what the questions are like.

Answer the Easy Ones Before the Hard Ones

This gives you more time to think of answers to the hard ones. It also ensures that you won't leave out any questions whose answers you know.

Eliminate the Wrong Answers

If you aren't sure of an answer, start by eliminating the choices that are obviously wrong. This gives you fewer possibilities to choose from—fewer chances to make a mistake.

Answer All the Questions

If time is running out, guess at the answers to the multiple-choice questions you've skipped, the ones you've found hardest. You have a better chance of getting credit by guessing than by leaving something blank.

Check Your Answers

Reread each question and its answers to make sure you really understood them and chose correctly. Also, make sure you haven't marked any wrong choices by mistake—haven't marked B when you knew the answer was C, for example.

Sample Multiple-Choice Questions

Directions Try your hand at answering these multiple-choice questions.

1. "The Woman Pharaoh" is about a woman who ruled ancient
   - **A.** Greece.
   - **B.** Rome.
   - **C.** Egypt.
   - **D.** Persia.

2. When Hatshepsut traveled, she
   - **A.** went alone.
   - **B.** dressed as a man.
   - **C.** learned the language of each country she visited.
   - **D.** enjoyed herself.

3. Who did Hatshepsut marry?
   - **A.** The man she was in love with.
   - **B.** A man who built a temple for her.
   - **C.** A stranger who had been picked out for her.
   - **D.** Her half-brother.

4. Which statement about Hatshepsut is a fact?
   - **A.** She was greater than Cleopatra.
   - **B.** She was a goddess.
   - **C.** She had more monuments built than any other queen of hercountry.
   - **D.** She was killed by her half-brother.

5. Which is not a theory about how Hatshepsut's reign ended?
   - **A.** She ruled until she died of old age.
   - **B.** She passed the crown peacefully to her nephew.
   - **C.** Her nephew had her killed so that he could take over.
   - **D.** She had to give up the throne when she married her boyfriend.

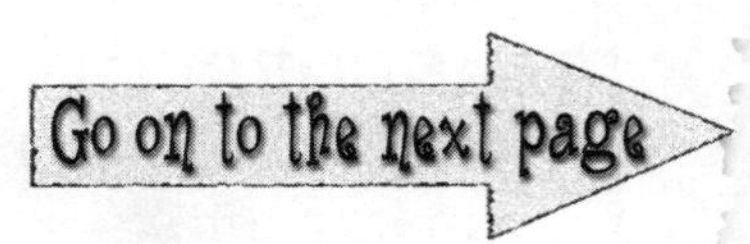

Check Your Answers

Match your answers with those of the pros! Here are the correct answers and the reasons why answers were either correct or incorrect.

1. "The Woman Pharaoh" is about a woman who ruled ancient
   A. **INCORRECT** The first sentence tells you that this is not the case.
   B. **INCORRECT** The first sentence tells you that this is not the case.
   C. **CORRECT** The first sentence gives you this information—and you may know that pharaoh was a word for an ancient Egyptian rule.
   D. **INCORRECT** This is incorrect for the same reason A and B are.

2. When Hatshepsut traveled, she
   A. **INCORRECT** Not likely! Ancient rulers usually traveled with large groups of courtiers and servants.
   B. **CORRECT** Odd as it seems today, she felt she had to put on a fake beard and male clothing to get respect from other rulers.
   C. **INCORRECT** There's nothing in the article about this. (Cleopatra was known for learning languages, though.)
   D. **INCORRECT** She might have enjoyed herself, but we don't know that from this article. This isn't the most specific, relevant answer to the question.

3. Who did Hatshepsut marry?
   A. **INCORRECT** Her boyfriend, Senemut, was a member of her court, but not high-ranking enough for her to marry.
   B. **INCORRECT** Senemut built a temple for her, but she didn't marry him.
   C. **INCORRECT** Her marriage was arranged, but it wasn't to a stranger.
   D. **CORRECT** It was the custom for ancient Egyptian rulers to marry their siblings, in order to keep the royal line "pure."

4. Which statement about Hatshepsut is a fact?
   A. **INCORRECT** The relative greatness of rulers is opinion, not fact. It can't be proven, only argued.
   B. **INCORRECT** It is a fact that she was worshipped as a goddess, but it is not a fact that she was a goddess.
   C. **CORRECT** This is stated in the third-from-last paragraph of the article.
   D. **INCORRECT** This is one theory. It hasn't been proven.

5. Which is not a theory about how Hatshepsut's reign ended?
   A. **CORRECT** Her rule ended early, when her nephew came of age.
   B. **INCORRECT** This is one of the theories stated in the article, so it is not one that is not stated.
   C. **INCORRECT** This is the other theory stated in the article.
   D. **INCORRECT** You already know from Question 3 that she didn't marry her boyfriend.

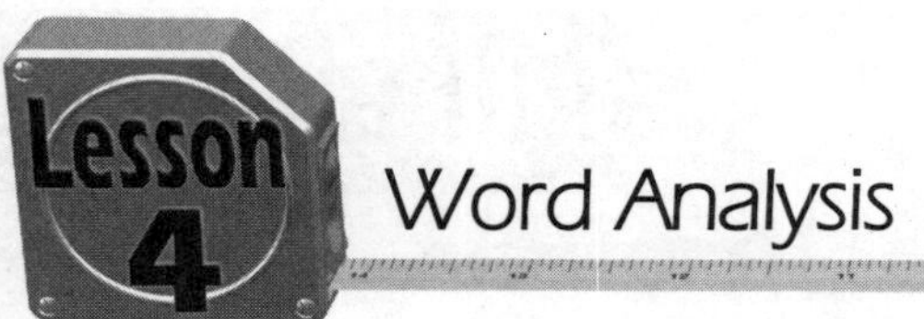

Word Analysis

Word Origins

A word's origin is its history. Words change over time. Their meanings, spellings, and pronunciations can all change. Words can enter one language from another language. Many words in English originated in other languages, such as French, Latin, Greek, and Anglo-Saxon. Other words came from the names of people or places.

For example, where does the word *language* come from? It entered English during the Middle Ages—about 1250-1300. It came from the French word *langue*, which means "tongue." The French word, in turn, came from the Latin word *lingua*, which means—you guessed it—"tongue." (In English today, a language can still be called a tongue.)

Knowing how a word got its meaning can give you a better understanding of that word and related words.

Activity

Directions Answer the questions in the blanks.

1. What is an archaeologist?

   A person who find things from a pirod long ago.

2. What is the origin of the word *archaeologist*? Look it up in a dictionary.

   The word means A scientist who studies archaeology.

3. List other words ending in *-ist*. What do they mean?

   A zoologist which means The scientist who specitizes animals.
   A scientist who studies Biology

Go on to the next page

Activity continued

4. An ancient Egyptian temple was later called "Deir el Bahari." What does that name mean and what is its origin? Reread paragraph 6 of the article to find out.

____

____

____

____

5. Hatshepsut served as co-pharaoh with her half-brother. What does *co-pharaoh* mean? What are the origins of its two main parts?

____

____

____

____

1. Which of the following words had its origin in ancient Egypt?

   A. pharaoh

   B. throne

   C. power

   D. queen

2. The word ***mummy*** comes from an old Persian word, ***mum***, meaning "wax." Why would a mummy be called "wax"?

   A. Wax is used for candles.

   B. The Egyptians preserved mummies by using wax and other substances.

   C. Part of the word ***mummy*** meant "wax."

   D. There is no logical reason; it was an accident.

3. Which word comes from a Greek word meaning "chief builder"?

   A. hieroglyph

   B. temple

   C. architect

   D. pharaoh

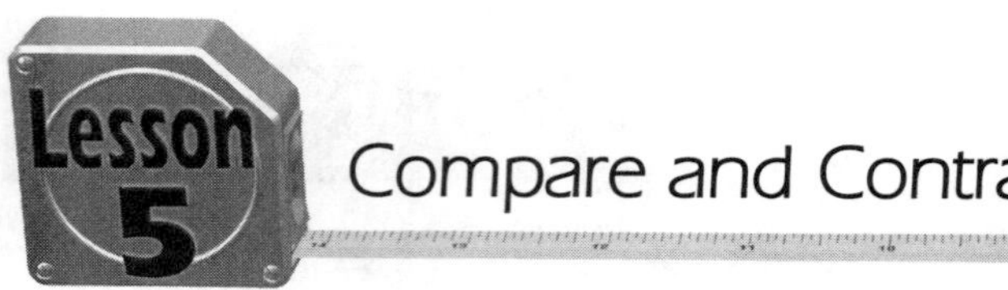

Lesson 5 Compare and Contrast

When you compare people, places, or things, you show how they are alike. When you contrast people, place, or things, you show how they are different. For example, if you were comparing Greece and Egypt, you might say, "Both were ancient civilizations." If you were contrasting them, you might say, "Egypt was an earlier empire."

In "The Woman Pharaoh," the author compares and contrasts Cleopatra and Hatshepsut and comes to the conclusion that Hatshepsut was greater.

Cleopatra

Hatshepsut

Activity

A. **Directions** Read the chart below from "The Woman Pharaoh." Then answer the questions.

WHO WAS THE GREATEST EGYPTIAN QUEEN?

HATSHEPSUT or CLEOPATRA

Hatshepsut	Cleopatra
HOME TURF	
Thebes, Egypt	Alexandria, Egypt
ANCESTRY	
Egyptian	Macedonian
YEARS IN POWER	
21 (1479-1458 B.C.)	21 (51-30 B.C.)
FASHION STYLE	
Dressed like a man	Dressed to attract men
REPUTATION AS A BEAUTY	
Underrated	Overrated
FAMOUS BOYFRIEND	
Senemut, royal courtier	Julius Caesar, Roman emperor
LEADERSHIP STYLE	
Helped rebuild Egypt after it fell to the Hyksos	In power when Egypt fell to Rome
SPECIAL TALENT	
Great self-promoter and politician	Could speak several languages
CIRCUMSTANCES OF HER DEATH	
Possibly murdered by Tuthmosis III	Possibly committed suicide by snake bite
PLAYED IN FILM BY	
None, but we'd pick Lucy Lawless	Elizabeth Taylor and others

Activity continued

1. Which queen came first in history? What were the dates of her reign?

The first queen was Hatshepsut 1479 - 1458 B.C

2. Describe what you think Hatshepsut would have worn to a royal function. Describe what you think Cleopatra would have worn.

I think Hatshepsut would wear a suit
Cleopatra would wear a dress

3. Look at the leadership style of both queens. Based on this information, why would the author conclude that Hatshepsut was the greater queen?

Hatshepsuit because she help Egyty

4. Look at the special talent of each queen. Which do you think would be more useful for keeping a queen in power?

Hatshepsuit because she can promote thing.

5. Who would you choose to play each queen in a movie? Explain how each actor is like each queen.

Cleopatra because she likes to dress pretty

6. Think about the qualities a person needs to rule a country. How do you think Hatshepsut and Cleopatra were alike in those qualities?

1. In what way were Hatshepsut and Cleopatra exactly the same?
   A. They have both been played by movie stars.
   B. They both ruled for 21 years.
   C. They were both murdered.
   D. They were equally great rulers.

2. One way Hatshepsut clearly outdoes Cleopatra is in
   A. being a skillful queen.
   B. marrying wisely.
   C. dying a natural death.
   D. being a native Egyptian.

3. One way Cleopatra clearly outdoes Hatshepsut is in
   A. being a skillful queen.
   B. having a good boyfriend.
   C. learning languages.
   D. dressing interestingly.

Cause and Effect

A cause is the reason why something happens. An effect is the thing that happens. For example, lack of rain can cause crops to die. Lack of rain is the cause; crop failure is the effect.

A cause can have more than one effect. For example, lack of rain can also cause lawns to turn brown. In some areas, it can cause desert plants to start growing in areas of grassland plants.

An effect can have more than one cause. For example, if crops die, lack of rain might be only one cause. Another cause might be poor planning by the farmer. Another cause might be lack of money, which keeps the farmer from being able to buy the best equipment.

Activity

Directions Read the article below, and answer the questions.

Can Koalas Survive?

Threatened by humans, these cuddly creatures head for new homes.

This cute koala is safe in the hands of a scientist. It's going to a new home where there are many eucalyptus trees that it can live in. But many other koalas aren't so lucky. Australia's eucalyptus trees are disappearing. Koalas' survival is in such jeopardy that in May, the United States officially listed them as threatened species. Read on to find out about this koala's journey—and the problems other koalas face.

About a hundred years ago, there were no koalas living on French Island, Australia. Then, according to legend, a man brought a couple of koalas to the island as a gift for his girlfriend. Those koalas' descendants now number about 800. The island's koala population could double every three years. The problem: Each koala eats about 2 ½ pounds of eucalyptus leaves every day. Too many koalas would quickly strip the trees on the island bare and all the animals would starve. The solution: Every year the government of Victoria (the Australian state that includes French Island) moves about 200 koalas—such as the one on the previous page—from the island to the mainland.

Activity continued

The journey begins as park rangers take the koalas from their homes in the trees. "We place a rope with a knotted loop at the end over the koala's head," says ranger Scott Coutts. "We get a flag on a pole above the koala and shake it. The koala backs away from the flag. Then we gently guide the animal down with the rope."

On the ground, rangers—who usually wear gloves for protection against sharp claws and teeth—put the koalas into wooden crates. The rangers attach blue tags to the animals' ears. The tags help scientist track released animals. After a short boat ride from the island to the mainland, wildlife officers take over the move. They transport the koalas to forests where there are enough species of eucalyptus trees to support the koalas.

Moving koalas ease the overpopulation problem on French Island. It also restores koalas to some mainland areas. But there is a much bigger koala problem in Australia that relocation can't solve.

Koalas are running out of places to live throughout their Australian home. Millions of koalas once roamed the mainland. But by the early 1900s, hunters had shot most of them—to make coats from their fur. Killing koalas is now illegal. But the koala population continues to decrease as human homes and malls gobble up the eucalyptus forests. People trying to solve the koala problem do not always agree.

"There is a conflict between trying to protect koalas and the expansion of towns," says Alan Crouch, a government wildlife expert in Victoria.

Relocation relieves population pressure in places such as French Island. But koalas need forests with the right mix of eucalyptus species, or they won't eat. The forest also must be large enough to support a healthy population. As forests are cut, such areas become harder to find.

"The remaining forests must be protected and trees must be replanted," says Ann Sharp of the Australian Koala Foundation. "Right now that is not being done."

Australians hope to solve this problem before koalas run out of space—and time.

Activity continued

1. According to legend, what caused koalas to live on French Island?

   A man brough koalas to his house

2. What official action by the United States was an effect of the decline in the koala population?

   Because it koalas are threatened

3. What happens to koalas if there aren't enough eucalyptus trees?

   Koalas will die because they will not food.

4. Why do rangers wear gloves when handling koalas?

   Because koalas live have sharp teeth and claws

5. What caused koala hunting to be declared illegal?

   Because koals

6. If there were too many koalas on French Island, what effect would it have on the eucalyptus trees?

   koalas will eat all the food and die

7 What would the effect in Question 6 cause?

   koalas eat all the food

1. One cause of the decline in eucalyptus trees is that

   A. koalas are running out of places to live.

   B. forest land is being cleared for malls .

   C. koalas won't eat unless the mix of eucalyptus trees is just right.

   D. koalas have stopped liking eucalyptus.

2. Why do the rangers attach blue tags to the koalas' ears?

   A. So they can track the animals' movements.

   B. So they will know which koalas to kill and which to take to zoos.

   C. So the koalas will obey their signals.

   D. So each person will know which koala is his or her own pet.

3. What is the effect of relocating koalas from French Island?

   A. It makes French Island more crowded.

   B. It angers people on the island.

   C. It angers people on the island.

   D. It eases population pressure on the koalas.

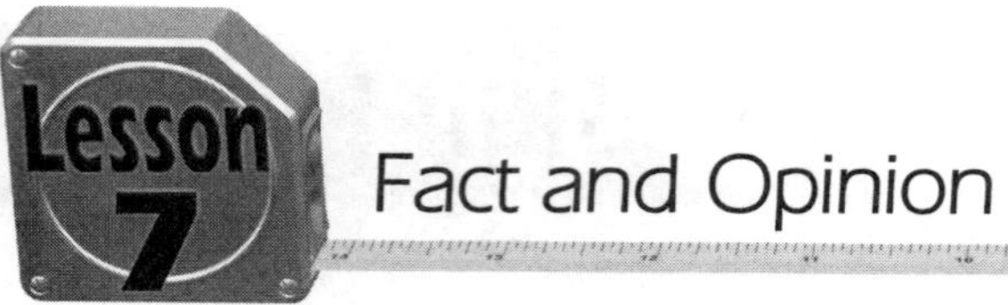

Lesson 7 Fact and Opinion

A fact is something that can be proved. For example, it is a fact that koalas live on French Island in the state of Victoria, Australia.

An opinion is a personal belief or judgment. It cannot be proved. If you say, "Koalas are the cutest animals on Earth," that is an opinion. It's true for you, but there is no factual evidence that can prove it. Even if every fact about every animal on Earth could be known, opinions would still differ about which is the cutest. Cuteness is a matter of taste. Matters of taste are opinions.

Activity

Directions Write "Fact" or "Opinion" on the blank following each statement.

1. Saving koalas is more important than building malls.

   Opinion ______________________

2. There are about 800 koalas on French Island.

   Fact ______________________

3. Every year, the government moves about 200 koalas off the island.

   Fact ______________________

4. Koalas and kangaroos are two animal species that are native to Australia.

   Fact ______________________

5. The koalas on French Island all descended from one pair of animals that a man brought to the island.

   Fact ______________________

Activity continued

6. Bringing those koalas to the island was a mistake.

Opinion

7. Australia has lots of problems aside from koalas.

fact

8. Australia has lots of problems that are more important than koalas.

Opinion

9. Kangaroos deserve less attention than koalas.

______

10. If koala hunting had not been made illegal, there would be no koalas left in the world today.

______

1. Which of the following is an animal fact?

   A. Tigers are better looking than lions.

   B. Koalas' favorite food is eucalyptus leaves.

   C. Kangaroos are everyone's favorite Australian animal.

   D. Ostrich meat tastes better than emu meat.

2. Which of the following is an opinion?

   A. If eucalyptus forests are cut, koalas will suffer.

   B. The koala in the picture is going to a new home.

   C. There is a conflict between trying to protect koalas and the expansion of towns.

   D. The safety of koalas should come before the desire of people for homes.

3. Think about the sentence, "Millions of koalas roamed Australia in the 1800s." Which of the following statements is true about that sentence?

   A. The sentence is a provable fact, because we can read eyewitness descriptions of the koalas from that time.

   B. The sentence is only an opinion, because we aren't living in the 1800s.

   C. The sentence is a fact, but we can't prove it.

   D. The sentence is an opinion, because there might only have been thousands, not millions, of koalas.

When you summarize, you restate the most important information or events from what you read. A summary is usually much shorter than the material it summarizes. In summarizing, concentrate on the major contents. Leave out minor facts and details.

Here is a summary of "Can Koalas Survive?"

> Koalas are a threatened species. They are in danger because the eucalyptus trees of Australia, their native continent, are disappearing. But some are in danger because the population of koalas can increase so rapidly. For instance, on the Australian island of French Island, the population of 800 koalas could double every three years. To solve this problem, the state government relocates about 200 koalas from the island each year. Park rangers take the koalas from their homes in the trees and transport them to the mainland. That eases the problem on French Island, but other Australian koalas aren't so lucky. The population is decreasing, as land needed for eucalyptus forests is developed for human uses. A conflict results: which is more important, koalas or shopping malls? If the problem isn't solved soon, it may be too late for the koalas.

Notice how much this summary leaves out. It leaves out the detailed description of how the park rangers get the koalas off the island. It leaves out the tagging of the koalas for scientific study. It leaves out the history of koala hunting. But it leaves in the most important thing: the crisis in the koalas population.

A. **Directions** Read the article. Write your responses on the lines.

Greece's Glorious Games

—Stephen Hanks

Okay, let's talk about this right from the start. At the ancient Greek Olympic Games, the athletes trained and competed in the nude—no uniforms, no sneakers, not even a loincloth.

Athletes who competed naked aren't the only difference between the ancient Greek Olympics and what we call the "modern" Olympic Games. In fact, the only similarities between the modern and ancient Games are that they are held every four years and that the champions are regarded as heroes.

1. Write a sentence or two summarizing the paragraphs above.

____

____

____

Olympian History

The first recorded ancient Olympic Games took place in Olympia, near Greece's southwest coast, in 776 B.C., when Nike was the goddess of victory, not the name of a shoe company. They continued to be held for the next 12 centuries in the same spot, which was considered a sacred and fertile place. The ancient Games were much more than athletic competitions.

They were also a celebration of the harvest and a religious festival to honor Zeus, the mythical king of the Greek gods. Cities throughout Greece were always fighting each other, but the Games were considered so important that every four years a truce was declared so citizens could compete in and attend the Games.

Activity continued

Until 724 B.C., the only Olympic event was a 200-yard footrace called the stade. In later Olympiads, the Greeks added events such as horse racing, boxing, wrestling, chariot racing, and the pentathlon, which included javelin and discus throwing among its five events. Between 20,000 and 50,000 people traveled to Olympia from all over Greek lands to watch the Games and see victorious athletes crowned with a wreath of olive branches, the ancient Greek equivalent of the gold medal.

2. Write a sentence or two summarizing the section above.

___

___

___

Olympian Archaeology

How do we know so much about events that occurred between 2,500 and 3,000 years ago? In the 1800s, French and then German archaeologists rediscovered Olympia, which had been destroyed by invaders more than 1,000 years before, and then buried by earthquakes and floods. In 1875, a German team began excavating the site and found much of the Olympic complex, including parts of buildings, racetracks, and statues. Over the years, they also found thousands of coins, iron and bronze objects, pottery, and inscriptions on monuments and tombs, which all helped to provide information about the Greek Games.

Researchers learned more about the Games from vases and other objects that the Greeks had illustrated with scenes from the competitions. In the centuries after the Games began, there are also many written descriptions of the Games that tell us how the athletes trained and what rules they had to follow. Pausanias, a writer from the 2nd century A.D., recorded many stories about the early Olympics. Pindar, a 5th-century

Activity continued

B.C. poet wrote victory odes honoring Olympic champions. He described victory as being an athlete's greatest goal and defeat his greatest shame. This doesn't sound much different from the way athletes and sports are written about today.

3. Write a sentence or two summarizing the section above.

____

____

____

Let The Games Begin!

Suppose there was a magazine 2,500 years ago called *Greek Sports Illustrated*? How would ancient sportswriters report on the Olympic Games? They might tell their readers that prior to each festival athletes had to train for 10 months. During the last month, athletes went to a town called Elis, the official host of the Games, where the *Hellanodikai* (judges) would make sure the athletes were ready to compete.

By the late 8th and early 7th centuries B.C., ancient sportswriters could write about the Olympics as a five-day sports festival. Boys between the ages of 12 and 18 competed in running, boxing, and wrestling events. Chariot and horse races were held in the *hippodrome* ("horse track" in Greek). The grueling pentathlon (meaning "five events"), held in the main stadium, would feature athletes competing in discus and javelin throwing, jumping, running, and wrestling.

The footrace events included the *stade*, the *diaulos*, which was a 400-yard race up and down the length of the stadium, and the *dolichos*, which was 24 lengths of the stadium, or almost 3 miles (try running that distance while naked!). After three days of such grueling events the athletes were ready to party. During a public banquet, they were given some meat from the morning's sacrifice.

Activity continued

Wrestling was introduced as an Olympic sport in 704 B.C. and wrestling quickly became fan favorites. A match continued until one wrestler threw his opponent to the ground three times, which could often take hours. Boxing matches, which became an Olympic event in 688 B.C., could also last all day and it was common for boxers to have their faces disfigured.

Wrestling and boxing were like playing patty-cake compared to the *pankration* (meaning "all strength")—a sport so violent even ESPN 2 probably wouldn't broadcast it. In this event, competitors were allowed to slap, kick, and trample each other. One legendary pankratiast was Arrakhion, who was declared the winner of a match that ultimately caused his death. This meant Arrakhion couldn't receive the olive wreath that was placed on the head of all Olympic winners on the last day of the Games. Ironically, the olive wreath was thought to bless the victor with long life.

4. Write a sentence or two summarizing the section above.

____

____

____

Activity continued

B. **Directions** Write a summary of the article as a whole.

Make Inferences

Sometimes, the ideas in a piece of nonfiction are stated directly. For example:

> Space exploration is a heroic challenge that has begun a bold new era in human history.

At other times, the author's message is not stated directly. It is implied. You, the reader, must find the author's ideas hiding behind the facts and details that the author gives you. You must infer the ideas. For example:

> Billions of people watched Neil Armstrong land on the moon on July 20, 1969. Hearts were lifted up across America and around the world as a human being set foot for the first time on another world. It was all of us who landed on the moon that day, not just one man.

In the paragraph above, the author never tells you directly that he thinks space exploration is heroic—but you can sense it in the author's words. You have made an inference about the author's attitude.

An inference is an intelligent guess that you make based on the evidence and on your prior knowledge. The evidence in a text might include facts, details, examples, anecdotes, quotations, and the author's choice of words.

Making inferences is something you do in real life all the time. If you go to the dentist, and the dentist looks back and forth from your X-rays to you and shakes her head with a slight smile, you infer, "Uh-oh, I've got cavities." The dentist hasn't yet said, "You've got two cavities," but you've made a good guess based on the evidence—and on your own knowledge of your candy-eating and toothbrushing habits!

Activity

Directions Read each passage below. On the lines below, write the inferences you are asked for. Then state your evidence.

1. On land, they waddle with a comical motion. They are so awkward at walking that they often travel by sliding along the ice on their bellies. And even though they are birds, you won't find them flying. They dive under the water, hunting for fish and other sea creatures, using their wings as flippers.

Inference: What kind of bird does the passage describe?

___

What is your evidence?

___

2. This state has the Cleveland Orchestra, the Cleveland Indians, and the Cincinnati Reds. It has Ohio State University, Ohio University, Miami University of Ohio, Oberlin College, Kenyon College, Antioch University, Case Western Reserve University, Ohio Wesleyan University, the University of Cincinnati, the University of Toledo, and many other colleges and universities.

Inference: What can you infer about Ohio from this passage?

___

What is your evidence?

___

3. Fellow citizens, we have remained silent too long! The previous mayor promised to build a new library on Fourth Street. She was elected on that promise. Four years have gone by, and the library has still not been built. Even in this election year, the mayor has taken no action at all on the promised library.

Inference: What is the speaker's view on the mayoral election?

___

What is your evidence?

___

Activity continued

4. My father first took me hiking when I was two years old. He had bought little hiking shoes for me—they must have been kids' size 4 or 5 or something like that—and had outfitted me with a vest and a peewee-size backpack. He himself wore grownup versions of the same gear. He held my hand as we walked on the dirt trails and hopped up and down the boulders. A hundred yards away, the Atlantic surf roared. Dad's strides seemed impossibly long. "Wait up, wait up!" I called as I slipped out of his grasp. He turned and stopped, smiling with pretend exasperation. I now know he was walking as slowly as he could. He was more patient with me than with anyone else.

   Inference: Make an inference about the father, the child, or both.

   ____

   What is your evidence?

   ____

5. Poetry is the most personal form of writing. A great poet reaches down into the deepest hidden regions of the soul. Feelings of hate, love, rage, forgiveness, despair, or faith are compressed into the fewest, and most beautiful, words possible. Then, they are shared with strangers. A poet will reveal a secret to thousands of strangers that he would not tell to a single friend.

   Inference: Make any inference from this passage.

   ____

   What is your evidence?

   ____

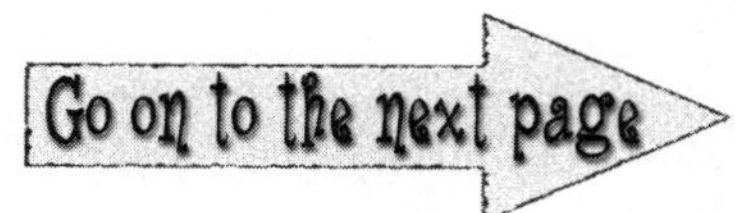
Go on to the next page

1. What can you infer about the place where the father and child hiked?
   - **A.** There were wild animals nearby.
   - **B.** It was too dangerous for a parent to take a child.
   - **C.** It was at the seashore of the East Coast.
   - **D.** There had been a lot of rain recently.

2. Which sentence contains evidence for the answer to Question 1?
   - **A.** My father first took me hiking when I was two years old.
   - **B.** Dad's strides seemed impossibly long.
   - **C.** I now know he was walking as slowly as he could.
   - **D.** A hundred yards away, the Atlantic surf roared.

3. What does the evidence show about the author of the paragraph on poetry?
   - **A.** The author is a woman.
   - **B.** The author is a poet.
   - **C.** The author spent a long time working on the paragraph.
   - **D.** The author knows and loves poetry.

Directions: Read the article and answer the questions.

Invasion of the Jellies
By Dewey Gram

They're headless, heartless, bloodless and brainless, and 95 percent water. But they're animals nonetheless, and many have a sting you'll never forget.

Last summer thousands of these pulsating blobs suddenly blossomed like weird undersea flowers off all three U.S. coasts.

Jellyfish! Whole armadas of them were sliding up through the surf to slime beaches from Cape Cod to Baja. Why the sudden abundance? Will they return?

No one knows for sure, but one thing is certain: There are a lot of these strange looking creatures floating around out there.

They're Baaaack!

Jellyfish begin their lives on the ocean floor. When they mature, they break free of the bottom to become floaters, or medusas.

They can move up and down by contracting their bells, in a form of jet propulsion. But to get around, most rely on tides and currents, or are blown by wind. The Portuguese man-of-war, for example, catches the breeze with a bladderlike float that extends as much as six inches above the waterline.

As jellyfish travel, their underwater "fingers" trap and sting tiny animals called zooplank for food.

Giant Invaders

While most are harmless to humans, that does not stop their size and appearance from scaring folks.

Off San Diego last year, swimmers and fisherman encountered the giant purple jellyfish. Last appearing in large number along the San Diego shoreline in 1989, it is the largest invertebrate (spineless) animal discovered in the 20th century. It can be three feet across, with tentacles 30 feet long.

Last year's invaders were smaller–about dinner-plate size with 10-foot tentacles–but big enough to scare swimmers.

Go On

East Coast Is Attacked Too

Jellyfish also invaded the Atlantic coast. Thousands of brownish-purple jellies called lion's manes (***Cyanea capillata***) washed up on the beaches of Cape Cod, Rhode Island and Connecticut. Meanwhile, squadrons of milky white East Coast sea nettles (***Chrysaora quiniquecirrha***) made life miserable for swimmers in Chesapeake Bay.

Dr. Lawrence Madin, chairman of the biology department at Woods Hole Oceanographic Institute in Woods Hole, Mass., attributed the New England outbreak to several factors, including food, water temperature and "maybe just winds blowing more up on the beach where people see them."

Gulf Jellies

On the Gulf of Mexico coast, the small but painfully potent watery jellyfish (***Pelagia noctiluca***), a purplish, glow-in-the-dark globster, also washed up in large numbers.

"We have a theory," said Dr. Monty Graham, senior marine scientist at Alabama's Dauphin Island Sea Laboratory, "that a warm current moved a trapped population of the jellyfish north from the Yucatan" peninsula in Mexico. Will this summer bring the dreaded jellies? "We have no idea where it comes from or where it goes," says Debbie Zmarzly, a specialist at the Birch Aquarium at the Scripps Institution in San Diego. "It's one of science's great little mysteries."

1. It is a fact that

   A. thousands of brownish-purple "lion's manes" washed up on New England beaches.

   B. jellyfish are scarier than bees or wasps.

   C. all swimmers hate jellyfish.

   D. jellyfish will return next season.

2. Which of the following is an opinion?

   A. The giant purple jellyfish is a large invertebrate.

   B. A mature, floating jellyfish is called a medusa.

   C. Jellyfish lack hearts and brains.

   D. Wind is responsible for the sudden appearance of so many jellyfish on beaches.

3. Which is ***not*** an effect caused by the sudden appearance of jellyfish on beaches?

   A. People get scared.

   B. When jellyfish mature, they float free.

   C. A child may receive a painful sting.

   D. Scientists ask why it happened, and search for answers.

4. The lion's mane and the sea nettle are both jellyfish, but in contrast to the lion's mane, the sea nettle is

   A. harmless.

   B. smaller.

   C. lighter in color.

   D. a faster swimmer.

5. Which statement is an inference supported by evidence in the article?

   A. Jellyfish begin their lives on the ocean floor.

   B. The author loves jellyfish.

   C. Jellyfish are stupid creatures.

   D. The Portuguese man-of-war is the best-known kind of jellyfish.

How to Write a Short Response

What's Expected on the Test

In the last group of lessons, you learned how to answer multiple-choice questions. Now, you will learn how to answer short-answer questions. The short-answer question is another type of question you will find on the Ohio Proficiency Test.

In this type of question, you are not given a set of answers to choose from. You must do some independent thinking. However, you may return to the article to find details that will help you write your answer.

Test-Taking Strategies

Make Sure you Understand the Question

Read the question carefully. Read it more than once. Underline key words and phrases. These include words and phrases that signal the thinking skill you are being asked for, such as *compare and contrast, analyze cause and effect, summarize, state an opinion, state a fact, infer, make an inference,* or *provide evidence*.

Make Sure Your Answer Fits the Question

You will lose credit if you don't answer the specific question. For instance, if you are asked to make an inference, don't state a fact that is already stated in the reading passage. If the question asks about the size of a type of jellyfish, don't write about whether the jellyfish is poisonous or not.

Be Complete

Sometimes, a question asks you to do more than one thing. Be aware of whether your question has more than one part. Then, check to be sure you have answered each part.

Be Clear

Don't fudge. State your response directly. Use strong, specific words. Ask yourself, Would I understand this if I were reading it?

Be Accurate

Get all your facts right. If you are asked for the Latin name of a species of jellyfish, make sure that you write the Latin name of that species and not a different species mentioned in the article. Make sure you spell the Latin name right. Make sure you capitalize correctly. Go back to the article to check details.

READING GUIDE

Directions Read the following article. Then read the short-answer question that follows it. Use the key strategies and the questions on the right of the article to help you answer the question.

Ready, Set, Rescue!

A powerful rip current suddenly swept Shayden Goode away while he was swimming at the beach in his hometown of Cronulla, Australia, six years ago. "I couldn't see much because the waves were high, so I waved my
1 arms," he recalls. As the fast-moving water carried him out to sea, he struggled, frightened and growing tired.
2 Suddenly a lifeguard arrived on a paddleboard. "He saved me," Shayden says.

People hit the beach almost year round in Australia, enjoying the mild weather and thousands of miles of coastline. But frequent rip currents and rough surf can mean danger. So Australians formed the world's first lifesaving clubs about a hundred years ago. These clubs train the country's famous surf lifesavers, who rescued almost 13,000 people last year. Some lifesavers become paid
3 lifeguards, but most patrol the beaches as volunteers. Lifesavers and other club members sharpen their skills in
4 contests that turn rescue drills into sport.

Kids as young as 7 can join the clubs as "nippers," or junior members. They learn to play safely in the surf; later they learn rescue skills. At 13, they can earn lifesaving certificates, a step toward gaining the Bronze medallion that all lifesavers must have. To earn a medallion, kids
5 must be 15 and pass advanced rescue and fitness tests. Every Sunday during Australia's spring and summer—October through February—620 nippers in the Cronulla Surf Life Saving Club meet at the beach. There they learn lifesaving and survival skills. "I used to get scared when I got caught in big waves," says Erin Payne, 14, of Kirrawee. "Now I know to hold my breath and dive
6 under them. When the waves end, I swim back to shore."

GUIDED QUESTIONS

1 What **prediction** can you make from the first two sentences?

2 **Form a picture** of the action in your mind. What do you see?

3 Is the information in this paragraph **fact or opinion?**

4 **Compare and contrast** a rescue drill with a sport.

5 **Link** these age requirements **to your own experience and knowledge**. Are they realistic?

6 **Check your understanding:** What is Erin's strategy? What does it achieve? Form pictures in your mind to help you understand.

Go on to the next page

READING GUIDE

It's not all work: The nippers also play rescue games and compete in swimming, running, and paddleboard races. Sometimes they find unexpected companions in the water. "I've been out with dolphins," says Sarah Rayner, 14, of Cronulla. "One jumped over the back of my
7 paddleboard."

The Cronulla nippers compete against other lifesaving clubs. The New South Wales state championship is the highlight of the season for them: They have taken first place three years in a row. One of the champion nippers is Shayden, now 14, who once nearly drowned and today
8 holds his own lifesaving certificate.

Sample Short-Answer Question

9 **1.** Based on the article, what aspects of learning lifesaving are fun and what aspects are serious?

____

____

____

____

GUIDED QUESTIONS

7 **Make an inference** about Sarah's experience.

8 **Summarize** the main points of the article.

9 **Notice** that this question has two parts. In your answer, did you show both things that are fun and things that are serious?

Activity

Directions Write your answer to the short-response question.

Self-Evaluation

Ask yourself:

- Is my answer complete? Have I shown both things that are fun and things that are serious?
- Does my answer show that I understood what I read?
- Is my reasoning sound?
- Is my answer well-detailed, and are the details relevant to the question?

How Your Response Will Be Evaluated

Teachers will use a rubric to evaluate your response. A rubric is a list of criteria for scoring the answer. Criteria are standards for measuring how well something is done.

Your response will be scored on a scale of 0-2. If you are given a score of 2, you've done the best possible job.

Short-Answer Rubric

Score	Criteria
2	• Is complete and appropriate • Demonstrates a thorough understanding of the reading selection • Indicates logical reasoning and conclusions • Is accurate, relevant, comprehensive, and detailed
1	• Is partially appropriate • Contains minor flaws in reasoning or neglects to address some aspect of the item or question • Is mostly accurate and relevant but lacks comprehensiveness • Demonstrates an incomplete understanding of the reading selection or inability to make coherent meaning from the text
0	• Indicates no understanding of the reading selection or item

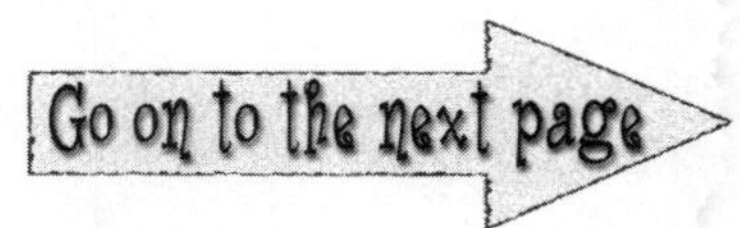

Question

1. Based on the article, what aspects of learning lifesaving are fun and what aspects are serious?

Sample Response

Playing in the surf, playing rescue games, competing in swimming, running, and paddleboard races, seeing dolphins, and winning championships are fun. Learning the lifesaving skills is serious, and so is being tested on them.

Evaluation

This is a 2 response. The writer has understood what the question asks for, and has included both the fun and serious aspects of the experience, using comprehensive details from the article.

Activity

Directions Look again at your own answer. Using the rubric, write your evaluation of your answer on the lines below.

____

____

____

____

____

Critique and Evaluate Organization

When you critique a text, you discuss it critically. When you evaluate a text, you examine it and judge it. In other words, "critique and evaluate" means "think about it carefully and discuss how good you think it is, and why."

In this lesson, you will be focusing on critiquing and evaluating the organization of an article. Organization simply means how the article is put together—how it flows from topic to topic, idea to idea. Organization is arrangement or order. If you have ever made an outline of a paper you have written, the outline showed the organization of the paper.

Organizational Structures

There are a few basic ways of organizing an article, ways you'll see again and again.

Time Order means putting events in the order they occurred. It's the natural order of storytelling, or narrative. Usually, time order goes from the earliest event to the latest. Occasionally, the order is reversed.

Cause and Effect Order shows how events cause one another to happen. It's related to time order, because causes occur before their effects. But it differs from time order, because not every event that occurs at one point in time is a cause of every event that occurs at a later point in time. Also, it's logical to track effects back to their causes.

Order of Importance may start with the most important point and proceed to less and less important points. Alternatively, it may start with the least important point and work its way toward the most important point.

Comparison and Contrast Order finds similarities or differences in the things being discussed. There are two primary modes of comparison and contrast order: (1) The author may discuss all the points of one of the things being compared, and then all the points of the other thing being compared; or (2) the author may discuss one point for both things being compared, then a second point for both things being compared, and so on.

Sometimes, an article uses only one of those forms of organization. At other times, the author combines more than one organizational pattern in the same article. For example, the article as a whole might be organized chronologically, but the points within each time period might be arranged in order of importance.

Go on to the next page

Activity **Directions** Read the article and answer the questions that follow.

A Quest for Better Vision: Spectacles Over the Centuries

—Clara Hemphill

The first eyeglasses were made by medieval monks who carved bits of quartz into magnifying glasses, riveted them together and perched them on their noses to magnify the tiny handwriting of manuscripts, historians say.

Gems had been used as magnifying glasses since ancient times, and the Roman emperor Nero is said to have gazed through an emerald ring to improve his view of gladiators in combat.

But spectacles represented a technological breakthrough because they freed the reader's hands.

And, because there was a lens for each eye, they provided stereotypic or three-dimensional vision.

"Eyeglasses give you depth perception, double your field of vision, and are less tiring than a magnifying glass," said Dr. Norman Medow, director of pediatric ophthalmology at Manhattan Eye, Ear, and Throat Hospital and an amateur historian of eyeglasses.

Roger Bacon, a scientist and Franciscan friar in England who was twice imprisoned by his order for "black magic," is often credited with making the first eyeglasses. The first written reference to spectacles is his "Opus majus," published in 1268.

But many historians attribute the discovery to monks in northern Italy. In Pisa, a Dominican monk, Alessandro della Spina, was making reading glasses at the end of the 13th century. The Chinese had spectacles in the 13th century as well, but they were used to shade eyes from the sun rather than to aid vision.

With the rise of the Venetian glass industry in the 14th century, glass lenses began to replace quartz. The invention to the printing press in the 1450s, the subsequent spread of books and the rise of literacy increased the demand for reading glasses. Eyeglasses were commonly sold on the streets in the 16th century, and professional guilds developed to control quality.

Activity continued

The original spectacles were only for the farsighted. In the beginning of the 16th century, eyeglasses were developed for the nearsighted as well. A 1517 portrait by Raphael depicts Pope Leo X holding a magnifying glass.

Keeping glasses on one's face was a trial. The pince nez (French for "pinches the nose") was uncomfortable and unstable, particularly for those engaged in active pursuits like making the king laugh.

Will Somers, Henry VII's court jester, had a suit of armor with spectacles riveted to the helmet, Alberta Kelly wrote in her book *Lenses, Spectacles, Eyeglasses and Contacts: The Story of Vision Aids.*

More conventional people attached lenses to their faces with ribbons and strips of leather.

"As long as you didn't sneeze, they would stay on your nose a while," said John Handley, the curator of the American Academy of Ophthalmology's museum of eyeglasses in San Francisco. "They weren't too comfortable, but if you didn't know any better, ignorance is bliss."

It was not until 1728 that a London inventor, Edward Scarlett, came up with a really good way to hold glasses on: temple pieces—strips of metal attached to the lenses with hinges that at first held the glasses at a 45-degree angle to the face.

George Washington bought a pair of glasses with hinged temple pieces for $75—a staggering sum in his day.

"The temple pieces were short when wigs were in fashion, because it would hurt to put a tight wig on top of them. The pieces evolved into wires long enough to hook over the ear when wigs went out of style in the 19th century," Mr. Handley said.

Benjamin Franklin is generally credited with the invention of bifocals. But London eyeglass makers were experimenting with the idea of fusing two lenses as early as 1760, according to Dr. Alvin and Virginia B. Silverstein, authors of *Glasses and Contact Lenses: Your Guide to Eyes, Eyewear and Eye Care.*

Go on to the next page

Activity continued

The idea of contact lenses dates to 1508 when Leonardo da Vinci submerged his face in a bowl of water and used the bowl as a refracting surface, Ms. Kelly wrote. At the end of the 19th century, the first contact lenses were made of glass and covered the whites as well as the iris. They were uncomfortable and could not be worn for more than a few hours.

Plastic lenses were developed in the 1930s, and by 1939, Hollywood movie makers were using contact lenses to change the color of actors' eyes to produce special effects like making someone look like an alien.

The prototype for corneal lenses, which cover only the center of the eye, was first developed by the American lens technician Kevin Tuohy in 1948. His lenses rode on a thin layer of tears, and were more comfortable than the larger ones that covered the white.

In the late 1950's, a Czech chemist, Otto Wichterle, invented a soft, water-absorbing plastic that seemed suitable for contacts. He made the first soft contact lenses in 1961 using a phonograph motor to a child's erector set, according to the *Encyclopaedia Britannica.*

Soft lenses were put on the market in 1971, and disposable lenses became available in 1987. About 31 million Americans wear contact lenses, the Contact Lens Council, a trade group, reports.

With the rise of vision-correcting eye surgery, "Fewer people in the future might use spectacles, but for sure their demise is exaggerated," said Dr. Medow, the pediatric ophthalmologist at the Manhattan hospital.

"There will always be a need for spectacles," he added, "either for residual correction after refractive surgery, or to add to our designer wardrobes."

Activity continued

1. What is the main form of organization used in the article? Where is it used?

   The main form of organization they used is cause and effect for the article and Where they use it is to aid the vision of farsighted and nearsighted.

2. Find another form of organization used in the article. Where is it used?

   Another form of organization used is time order And Where it is used to tell the date of people or famous people that was doing something at the same time as the eyeglass or contacts are being made.

3. How effective do you think the organization of the article is? Why?

   I think the article is very effective because it tells me alot of details and the organization is very helpful because makes everything in order, so it can makes sense.

4. Arrange the following names from the article in time order, from earliest date to most recent:

   - Benjamin Franklin 3
   - Kevin Tuohy 5
   - Nero 1
   - Leonardo da Vinci 4
   - Roger Bacon 2

   Review the article for clues.

   Nero, Roger Bacon, Benjamin Franklin, Leonardo da vinci, Kevin Tuohy.

Go on to the next page

Activity continued

5. Arrange the following events in order of importance, from most important to least important:

5 ◆ Nero watches gladiators fighting,
1 ◆ Alvin and Virginia B. Silverstein write a book about eyeglasses
4 ◆ soft contact lenses are put on the market
2 ◆ a monk in Italy makes reading glasses in the 1200s
3 ◆ a London inventor develops temple pieces for eyeglasses

Explain your ordering.

Alvin and Virginia B. Silverstein write a book about eyeglasses. A monk in Italy makes reading glasses in the 1200s. A London inventor develops temple pieces for eyeglasses, then soft contact lenses are put on the market. Nero watches gladiators fighting.

1. Which of the following comes first in time order?
   A. Roger Bacon writes about eyeglasses.
   B. Otto Wichterle invents soft contact lenses.
   C. George Washington buys glasses for $75.
   D. Dr. Norman Medow says, "Eyeglasses give you depth perception."

2. Which of the following comes last in time order?
   A. Nero looks through an emerald.
   B. Dr. Norman Medow says, "There will always be a need for spectacles."
   C. Leonardo da Vinci sticks his face in a bowl of water.
   D. Sunglasses are invented in China.

3. Which of the following comes first in cause-and-effect order?
   A. The earliest, whole-eye contact lenses are uncomfortable.
   B. Corneal lenses cover part of the eye and ride on a layer of tears.
   C. People often have trouble with their eyes.
   D. Eyeglasses improve vision, but can fall off and break.

4. What do you think would be the ***least*** effective form of organization for this article? Explain.

____

____

____

____

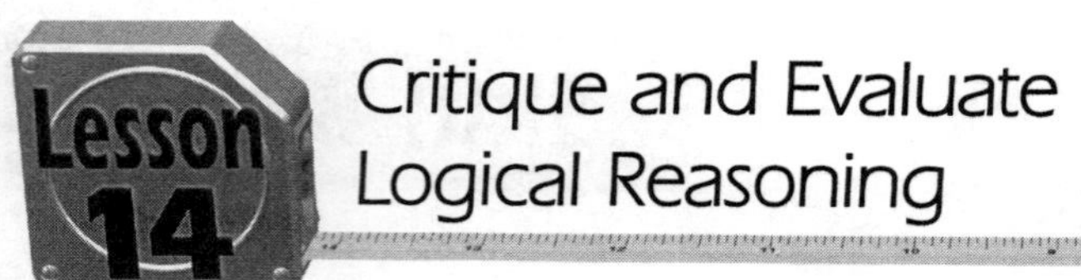

Lesson 14 Critique and Evaluate Logical Reasoning

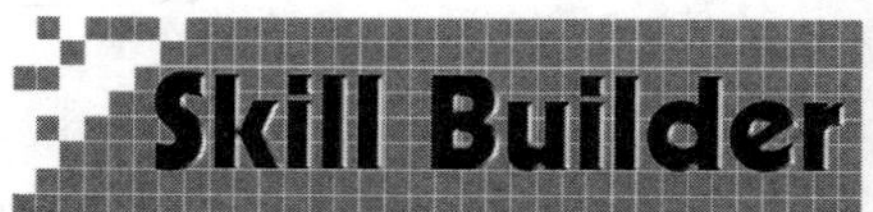

When you critique and evaluate a text for logical reasoning, you're examining and discussing how successfully the author supports his or her ideas. To be effective, a logical argument should be supported, or backed up, by reasons and evidence. These reasons and evidence should appeal to the reader's sense of logic, rather than only to the reader's emotions. Finally, the argument should not show fuzzy thinking. It should not be biased. It should not contradict itself by saying two conflicting things at once. It should not jump to conclusions—that is, reach conclusions on the basis of inadequate evidence. There should be enough solid evidence to convince the reader.

Activity

Directions Read each passage below and answer the questions.

A. Ohio is obviously the best state in the United States. That's why they call us the President State. Seven presidents have come from Ohio: Ulysses S. Grant, Rutherford B. Hayes, James A. Garfield, Benjamin Harrison, William McKinley, William Howard Taft, and Warren G. Harding. That's probably more presidents than any other state has had. And since the president is the most important person in the country, it follows logically that the state with the most presidents is the most important state.

1. Does the passage rely more on logic or on emotion?

____

2. What evidence does the author supply for his or her argument?

____

____

3. Is the reasoning in the passage fuzzy or valid? Discuss any logical flaws you find in it.

____

____

____

____

Activity continued

B. There have been several theories about why the dinosaurs disappeared. Some scientists have thought that the climate got colder when mountains formed, and that the huge reptiles couldn't survive the cold. Some say that movements of the earth's crust caused swamps to drain, and that this destroyed a large part of the natural habitat of dinosaurs. Or, maybe the dinosaurs were unable to compete with the mammals for food. Or, maybe the meat-eating dinosaurs like Tyrannosaurus Rex were such good hunters that they killed off all the plant-eating ones, and thus had no food left. The best new theory is that about 65 million years ago, a big asteroid crashed into the Earth and caused a sudden, long-term change in the climate. That's the theory I believe.

4. Does the passage rely more on logic or on emotion?

____

5. What evidence does the author supply for his or her argument?

____

____

6. Is the reasoning in the passage fuzzy or valid? Discuss any logical flaws you find in it.

____

____

____

____

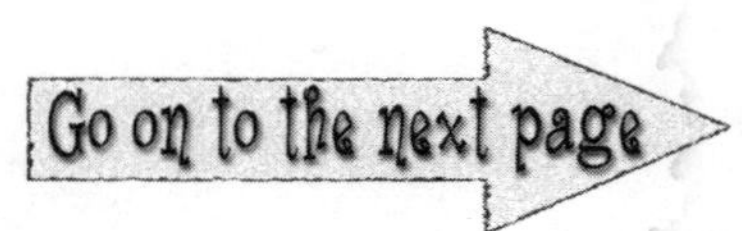

Activity continued

C. School should be year-round. This is why: by the time summer vacation is over, everyone has forgotten what they learned last year, and then they have to start all over again with review. You spend so much time reviewing what you already learned and forgot, that you don't have enough time to learn anything new. Summer vacation is boring for a lot of people, anyway. Sure, everyone acts like they're supposed to love summer vacation, but if you ask around, you'll find that a lot of kids don't do anything exciting at all, and really they're secretly glad to be back at school. School might be boring, but nothing is as boring as a summer off when you're sitting around in a hot apartment not doing anything but watching reruns, and all your friends are gone.

7. Does the passage rely more on logic or on emotion?

____

8. What evidence does the author supply for his or her argument?

____

____

9. Is the reasoning in the passage fuzzy or valid? Discuss any logical flaws you find in it.

____

____

____

____

Activity continued

D. What this country needs is a computer lab in every school. Of course, many schools already have computer labs, but that's part of my point: those schools have an unfair advantage over schools that lack computers. And why do some schools have computers and some not? The answer is one word: money. Schools in wealthy districts have an unfair advantage over schools in poorer districts. Students in poor districts do not have equal access to up-to-date educational facilities. This is most obviously true when it comes to computers. It costs a lot of money for a district to buy computers for all its schools. Many districts simply cannot afford it. What are they to do, send their graduates out into the new global economy ill-prepared? We cannot accept that answer. Instead, some way must be found of getting computers for poorer schools—whether through public funds or private.

10. Does the passage rely more on logic or on emotion?

____

____

11. What evidence does the author supply for his or her argument?

____

____

12. Is the reasoning in the passage fuzzy or valid?
Discuss any logical flaws you find in it.

____

____

____

____

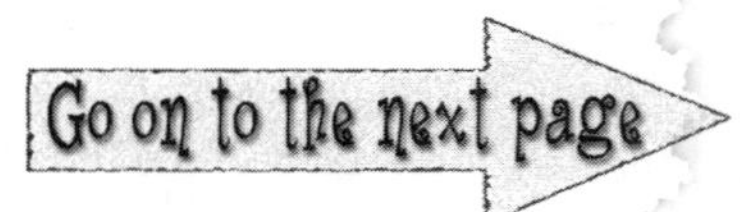

1. The statement "Down with the traitors who have led us to disaster!" is not an example of
   A. appeal to logic.
   B. appeal to emotion.
   C. fuzzy thinking.
   D. a statement unsupported by evidence.

2. Suppose you are arguing in favor of year-round school. Which of the following would be the strongest piece of evidence?
   A. You say, "I think I'd really like year-round school."
   B. Summer vacation is an old idea, not a new one.
   C. Teachers should not get such long vacations.
   D. Studies in several countries have shown that year-round school works.

3. Which piece of evidence would do most to support the theory that an asteroid crash 65 million years ago was responsible for the extinction of the dinosaurs?
   A. That theory makes the most exciting story; it sounds right.
   B. No evidence is found of swamp drainage shortly before the extinction of the dinosaurs.
   C. An underwater crater is found in the Gulf of Mexico, which is dated to 65 million years ago and seems to have been caused by an asteroid.
   D. A poll of scientists shows that 95% believe in the asteroid theory.

4. Suppose you want to write about why a certain state is the best. (It might be Ohio or a different state.) What kinds of evidence would you put in to convince readers?

____

____

____

____

Lesson 15 Recommend

What Is a Recommendation?

When you make a recommendation, you tell others whether you think a certain text is a good one for them to read. A recommendation can be either positive or negative (thumbs up or thumbs down). You might say, “I recommend this article,” or, “I highly recommend this article,” or, “I don’t recommend this article.”

A good recommendation goes beyond just saying, “I think you should read it,” or, “I think you should skip it.” The recommendation should also include reasons. For example, you might say, “I think you should read Helen Keller’s autobiography because it is as inspiring as it is well-written, and because it conveys a unique experience—that of being blind and deaf—better than any other source.”

Audience

The reasons in your recommendation might also include references to the tastes and interests and needs of the person you’re recommending the work to. You would not necessarily make the same recommendations to everyone. For example, you might recommend Helen Keller’s *The Story of My Life* to someone your own age who was interested in inspirational life stories. You wouldn’t recommend it to an eight-year-old, and you wouldn’t recommend it to someone who hated inspirational life stories. (Some people do!)

Purpose

To know whether to recommend a certain work to a specific person, you need to know that person’s purposes. What is that person looking for in a book or article? Why would he or she want to read this particular work? If possible, your recommendation should mention or relate to the person’s purposes. For example, you might say, “I think you’d love Helen Keller’s autobiography because you’ve said you’re interested in working with the visually impaired.” Or, “I think you’d love Helen Keller’s autobiography because it will show you that anyone’s problems can be overcome.” Different readers, different purposes, different recommendations.

Activity

Directions Choose one of the articles that you have read so far in this chapter. It might be an article you like, or one that you don't like. (It's better not to choose an article you are neutral about.) Write two recommendations about the article. Aim your recommendations at two very different people, with different purposes for reading.

Title of Article: ______________________________

1. Person: ______________________________

Purpose: ______________________________

Recommendation: ______________________________

____

____

____

____

2. Person: ______________________________

Purpose: ______________________________

Recommendation: ______________________________

____

____

____

____

1. To which person would you be ***least*** likely to recommend a biography of Julius Caesar?
   A. a student of military history
   B. a student of ancient history
   C. a student of the psychology of high achievers
   D. a student of computer science

2. You would most probably recommend an article on hairstyles to a person who
   A. had no interest in history.
   B. kept saying, "I hate my hair."
   C. was bald.
   D. had said, "I've got to find an article on Julius Caesar by tomorrow."

3. Your friend is upset because some thoughtless people have said mean things to her. Which article would you be most likely to recommend?
   A. "How to Find Anyone, Anywhere"
   B. "301 Great New Ideas for Soy Protein"
   C. "Block Out Negative Messages and Boost Your Self-Esteeem"
   D. "Get Over Stage Fright in Five Easy Steps!"

4. Select any of the four article choices from Question 3. Write a recommendation for that article. Address your recommendation to a specific person, stating why the article is or is not right for him or her. The recommendation may be either positive or negative. The person may be real or imaginary.

____

____

____

____

Lesson 16 Connect Content to Purpose

Any nonfiction topic can be written about in many different ways. The author chooses how to approach the topic according to what his or her purpose is.

For example, suppose five different writers are writing on the topic of flowers, each writer with a different purpose:

- Writer A's purpose is to provide information—facts and data about flowers.
- Writer B's purpose is to help readers understand the importance and beauty of flowers.
- Writer C's purpose is to help readers solve problems they might have in growing flowers.
- Writer D's purpose is to help readers figure out which flowers to plant in which areas of the United States.
- Writer E's purpose is simply to describe flowers in a way that readers will enjoy.

Here are examples of different kinds of details each writer might include.

Writer	Purpose	Detail
A	to held readers find out facts	The basic parts of a flower are the sepal, petal, stamen, and carpel.
B	to help readers understand	Flowers and bees are linked in a web of life: flowers need bees to spread pollen, and bees need flower nectar to make honey.
C	to help readers solve problems	Too much water can drown a flowering plant, although too little water can kill it too.
D	to help readers figure out how to do something	In zones with warm winters, you can plant bulbs in the fall.
E	to have readers enjoy	One April afternoon, I found a blaze of crayon color, a field of purple and orange and red and yellow wildflowers, beside an interstate highway.

Directions Read the article and answer the questions that follow.

Making Faces

—Leslie Birdwell

"Alas, poor Yorick!" cries Hamlet, the main character in one of William Shakespeare's most famous plays. Hamlet looks at the skull of his old friend, the court jester, and fondly remembers what Yorick was like when he was alive.

Although Hamlet could have easily described his dead friend's physical appearance from memory, could today's scientists and sculptors re-create Yorick's face simply by analyzing his skull? Yes, according to facial reconstruction experts, who can create distinctive features from fleshless skulls.

Gay Malin, a sculptor at the New York State Museum in Albany, New York, recently reconstructed the face of an unknown woman who died about 300 years ago. Archaeologists have named her Pearl after Albany's Pearl Street, where her remains were found in an almost forgotten cemetery. Why reconstruct the face of a 300-year-old skeleton?

"We wanted something people could relate to," explains Malin. "You can connect so much better to something that seems real."

Archaeologists Find a Pearl

During much of America's colonial period, Albany was a Dutch fort and trading post. After England gained control of Albany in the late 1600s, the Dutch Lutheran settlers were given a piece of land where they built a church and a cemetery.

"We were surprised when we found many graves at the site because we thought they had been moved when the church and cemetery were moved," says Charles Fisher, the New York State Museum archaeologist who directed the excavation. Unfortunately, the cemetery records had disappeared so it was impossible to identify the remains. The skeleton with the most complete set of bones became Pearl.

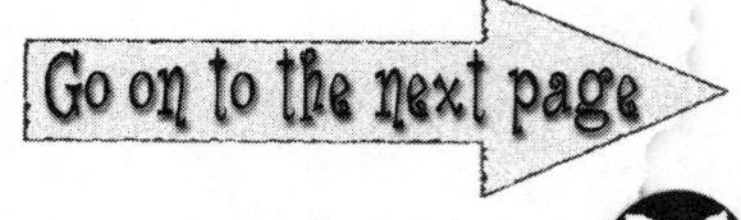

Activity continued

By analyzing skulls, scientists can determine people's gender and ancestry, their age when they died, and whether they died from a head injury. From the condition of the bones and teeth, scientists can also find out about their health. From looking at Pearl's skull and skeleton, scientists could tell that she was small (about 5-foot-1) and somewhat delicate. They could also tell that Pearl died in her 40s, had lost 60 percent of her teeth, and was probably descended from Europeans.

Reconstructing Pearl

After an anthropologist glued Pearl's skull fragments back together, Gay Malin could begin reconstructing her face. Since the sculpture is never made right on the original bones, Gay had to make a mold of Pearl's skull. First, she coated the skull with silicone rubber. After the rubber hardened, she peeled it off, leaving what looked like an inside-out mask. Gay then poured wet plaster into the rubber mold. When the plaster set, she peeled off the mold.

After placing glass eyeballs in the eye sockets, Gay started sculpting Pearl's face. She began by analyzing the data compiled from computer scans of people who were Pearl's size. Then Gay inserted tissue-depth markers, usually made of erasers or small wooden dowel rods, into 21 different spots on the skull. The markers gave Gay a guideline for how thick to make the flesh. Since Pearl's skull was small, the depth of the markers was based on a thin person's face. Gay then sculpted onto the skull features such as glands, pads of fat, and facial muscles, which together determine the outer surface of the face.

Pearl Gets a Personality

Now it was time to give Pearl's face some personality. Using the tissue-depth markers as a guide, Gay began sculpting the face with strips of clay. Since a skull can't tell a sculptor much about the shape of a person's nose or ears, Gay created "generic" ones based on the average height and width of the rest of Pearl's face.

Activity continued

Gay didn't want Pearl to look like a lifeless store mannequin, so she used many techniques to make Pearl's skin look real. She pressed a piece of soft deer hide into the damp clay to give the face texture. She also pressed crumpled paper towel and plastic wrap against the clay to give Pearl fine wrinkles.

Then it was time to make another mold out of silicone rubber. Why another mold? "You can't display a clay sculpture," says Gay, "because it will dent as soon as you touch it. You also can't paint on it, and when it gets dusty, the dust sticks." Gay painted the inside of the new mold with a glue-like material, let the glue harden, then peeled everything away to make a final cast of Pearl's face. She then painted the skin, popped in glass eyes, added synthetic hair (based on the hairstyle of the late 1600s), and topped it all off with a cloth cap of the kind Pearl might have worn.

Everyone in Albany, including the members of the local Lutheran church, were very excited when they saw the finished Pearl. "This kind of reconstruction," say Charles Fisher, "is about people and their relationship to the past." We still don't really know who Pearl was or even her true name, but Gay Malin's remarkable reconstruction has made her seem real to us. If only Gay had been around in Hamlet's time.

Activity continued

1. Find a sentence in the article that helps the reader find out facts or data.

   During much America's colonial period, Albany was Dutch fort and trading post.

2. Find a sentence in the article that helps the reader understand the subject more fully.

   He wanted something to have something people could relate to.

3. Find a sentence in the article that seems intended for the reader to enjoy.

   If only Gray had been in Hamlet's time,

4. State a problem that the article might help some reader solve.

   ____

   ____

5. Describe an imaginary reader who might find this article helpful in figuring out something. What would that "something" be?

   ____

   ____

   ____

   ____

1. What would be an author's purpose for writing this sentence: "Albany, the capital of New York State, was called Fort Orange when it was first settled by the Dutch in the early 1600s"?
   A. to help the reader find out information
   B. to help the reader figure out how to do something
   C. to help the reader solve a problem
   D. to have the reader enjoy

2. What would be an author's purpose for writing this sentence: "If you want to sculpt a face using the skull shape as a base, first make a mold of the skull, using silicone rubber"?
   A. to help the reader understand
   B. to help the reader figure out how to do something
   C. to have the reader enjoy reading
   D. to give the reader information–facts and data

3. Which sentence seems written for the reader to enjoy?
   A. Albany is the site of the State University of New York at Albany and several other institutions of higher learning.
   B. To get to Albany from New York City, you take the Thomas E. Dewey Thruway north.
   C. Pressing a piece of deer hide into the clay of a sculpted face will give the face texture.
   D. Looking at the finished sculpture of Pearl's face, you might very well expect her to wake up and exclaim, "Where am I?"

4. Review the article "Making Faces." What do you think was the author's main purpose? Explain your answer.

I think

____

____

____

Lesson 17 Vocabulary Development

The Suffixes *-ology* and *-ologist*

What is *archaeology*? It is the science that studies ancient cultures by digging up and examining their remains. You could guess the meaning of that word if you know that it is made up of a prefix, *archaeo-*, and a suffix, *-ology*. *Archaeo-* means ancient or very old. The suffix *-ology* means "the study of." It is used in the names of sciences and other fields of study.

From *-ology*, we get another suffix, *-ologist*. An "ologist" is a person involved in an "ology." An archaeologist is someone who practices archaeology—someone who studies ancient cultures by examining their remains.

Understanding Words Using *-ology* and *-ologist*

When you read nonfiction about special fields of knowledge or study, you will often come across new words containing the suffixes *-ology* or *-ologist*. Now that you know the meaning of these suffixes, you have a head start toward figuring out those new words.

Sometimes, words ending in one of these suffixes are easy to figure out. For example, most people could probably figure out that a criminologist is someone who studies crime. (Not someone who commits it, we hope!) It takes a little more knowledge to realize that a meteorologist is *not* someone who studies meteors. It's someone who studies weather.

After you have guessed the meaning of a new "ology" or "ologist" word, look up the word in a dictionary. By doing so, you'll not only learn the specific "ology" or "ologist" word, but you'll also learn a new prefix that is probably found in other words as well. For example, if you learn that *ethnology* is the study of cultures, you'll gain a better understanding of the words *ethnic* and *ethnicity*. In building your vocabulary, one word almost always leads to another.

Activity

Direction Build words by combining each prefix on the chart with the suffixes *-ology* and *-ologist*. Use a dictionary if necessary. The first example has been done for you.

Prefix	+ ***-ology***	meaning	+ ***-ologist***	meaning
eco-	ecology	the science of the relationship of living things to their environment	ecologist	a scientist who studies the relationship of living things to their environment
zoo-	zoology	The branch of biology that deals with animals.	zoologist	A scientist who specializes in zoology.
geo-				
bio-				
psych-	psychology	The scientific		
ornitho-	ornithology	The scientific study of birds.	ornithologist	A scientist who specializes in ornithology.

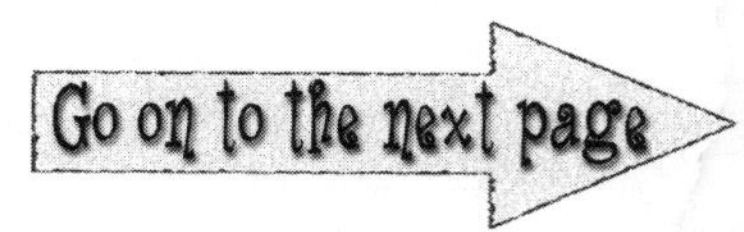

1. A ________ was called in to say whether the shiny stone they found was a rough diamond.

   A. musicologist

   B. mineralogist

   C. dermatologist

   D. radiologist

2. The prefix ***crypto-*** means "hidden." ***Cryptology*** is the study of

   A. codes and ciphers.

   B. the human mind.

   C. rocks and minerals.

   D. human cultures.

3. Astronomy is a real science–the study of stars and other bodies in outer space. Astrology is a false science–the study of ________.

   A. the lives of movie actors and actresses

   B. airplane design

   C. people's fates by looking at the stars

   D. planets

4. Look up the word ***neonatology***. Explains what it means and where it comes from.

   ____

   ____

   ____

   ____

   ____

How to Write an Extended Response

What's Expected on the Test?

A third type of question found on the Ohio Proficiency Test, in addition to multiple-choice and short-answer, is the extended-response question. It requires a more elaborate answer than the short-answer type. It usually requires more thinking than the short-answer type. In answering an extended-response question, you may return to the selection as many times as you need to.

Extended responses are usually several sentences long. Think of your extended response as a paragraph. It should be rich in detail and well-organized.

An extended-response question may ask you to retell or summarize—to put information from the selection in your own words.

An extended-response question may ask you to respond personally to the selection—to connect it to your own life and experience.

An extended-response question may ask you to write critically—to analyze the selection and evaluate its strengths and weaknesses.

Test-Taking Strategies

Understand the Question

Look for key words that tell you exactly what the question is asking for. Highlight those key words if you wish. For example, a question may say, "Evaluate the way the selection provides information," or, "How well do you think the selection provides information? Explain."

Plan Ahead

Rather than just starting to write your answer as soon as you have read the question, take time to think about what you want to say. Focus on the question mentally. Try out a couple of possible opening sentences. Think about what details you want to include. You might even find it helpful to outline your answer in advance. But make sure you leave time to actually write the answer! That's part of planning ahead, too.

Stay Focused

Don't stray from the topic. When you're writing a long answer, it's easy to trick yourself into writing a lot of words that are off the subject. If you have planned your answer, you should have a good idea of what you want to say. As you write, make sure to say that, and not other things. Make sure you answer the question that was asked, not some other possible question about the selection.

Organize Your Paragraph

Try to begin with a sentence that states the main idea of your answer. Then, try to make sure that your sentences, and their ideas, are logically connected to one another. Wrap the answer up with a concluding sentence, if time permits. A strong extended response is a flowing piece of prose, not a jumble of separate statements.

Use Transitions

The quickest way to lend unity to a paragraph—and therefore a good method to use on a test—is to include transitional words and phrases. Little words like *because, since, first, next, last, finally, before*, and *after* are signposts directing the scorer to the meaning of your answer.

READING GUIDE

Directions Use your reading strategies as you read the following article. Use the questions on the right to help you probe the article's meaning. After reading the article, read the extended-response question. Then, think about the question in relation to the article, and write your answer.

The History of Counting
—by Denise Schmandt-Besserat

Most of us take our modern counting system for
granted. We forget, or never seem to realize, that counting
1 had to be invented and evolved over time. The earliest
counting devices are notched bones made by hunters and
gatherers who lived about 15,000 years ago in what is now
the Middle East. Although we don't know what these
ancient people counted with the notched bones, these
counting devices may tell us *how* they counted. Because
each notch is similar to the next one and because there
never seems to be a total indicated on the bones, it is
likely that these people had not yet developed numbers.
2 Each notch probably stood for "and one more."

The counters found in the towns built by farmers
between 5,000 and 10,000 years ago were small tokens of
many shapes. Each token shape was used to count only
one item. For example, sheep were counted with disks, but
jars of oil were counted with egg-shaped tokens. (We know
this because the signs for sheep and oil in early Sumerian
writing pictured a disk and an egg shape.) This is known
as *concrete* counting. The early farmers used the tokens by
matching them with the number of things counted: one
3 disk indicated one sheep, two disks two sheep, and so on.

The invention of *abstract* numbers was the real
starting point of counting and is the one most of the world
uses today. We separate, or abstract, the idea of "one,"
"two," "three," and so on, from the thing we are counting.
4 Abstract numbers are infinite (meaning endless) and can
count anything.

GUIDED QUESTIONS

1 **Set a purpose:** Why are you reading this article? As you read, look for details that will help you fulfill your purpose.

2 **Make a prediction** about how counting might have been improved by later peoples.

3 **Form a picture** of the tokens in your mind. What do you see?

4 **Check your understanding**: What are abstract numbers? Read on to enhance your understanding of this difficult concept.

Go on to the next page

READING GUIDE

We owe the invention of abstract numbers to the Sumerians who lived in the first cities, in the southern part of present-day Iraq, about 5,000 years ago. In the illustration below, the clay tablet in the man's hand shows an account of 33 jars of oil. The sign on the right stands for "jar of oil." The other signs represent numbers. Each circle is 10, and each long sign is 1.

Why is this counting system different from the others? For the first time, number and things counted were separated, or abstracted. Sheep and jars of oil were finally counted using the same numbers! The first farmers invented tokens because counting is important when the community depends on knowing things like how many bags of grain to keep for planting the next harvest.

Once abstract numbers were invented, they were used widely in trade and in calculations needed for everyday
5 life. And with the greater use of numbers came the need for larger numbers.

In the country of Sumer, the most common large number used in everyday life was 60. It was called "the big one," which suggests that, at some time, it had been the highest number.

While the Sumerians' system was remarkable for the time, it had one drawback: It didn't have zero. In other words, the Sumerians had no sign to indicate "no value." They just left a space. Doesn't that make reading numbers a bit difficult? Look at number 204,501. How easy is it to
6 read without the zeros—2 4,5 1?

GUIDED QUESTIONS

5 **Connect ideas:** In different times and civilizations, were there similar reasons for improving the system of numbers?

6 What would life be like without zero? Think about a zeroless number system in **contrast** to our system.

READING GUIDE

The Sumerians' counting system was used for centuries. Why was such a complicated counting system used for so long? Perhaps it is easier to follow old ways of thinking than to come up with new ways.

But the Phoenicians, who invented the alphabet around 1500 B.C., came up with a new way. They used letters of their alphabet as numerals. By 500 B.C., the Greeks had borrowed the Phoenician system. The Greeks used 27 letters in their alphabet as numerals. The first nine letters were the numbers 1 through 9. The next nine letters were the tens, and the last nine letters were the hundreds. The last letter stood for 900.

By 300 B.C., the Romans improved on the system by reducing the number of signs to seven (I=1, V=5, X=10, L=50, C=100, D=500, M=1,000), what we call Roman
7 numerals. Once again, common numerals didn't reach beyond 1,000, indicating how rarely large numbers were used in everyday life in Rome. Today, we still use Roman numerals for showing dates on buildings, for numbering volumes and chapters in books, and when indicating the hours on some clocks.

But when we add, subtract, multiply, and divide, we use digits called Arabic numerals. And, of course, we write them as 0, 1, 2, 3, 4, 5, 6, 7, 8, and 9.

Where and when the Arabic numerals were invented is a mystery. Why then are the digits of our counting system called Arabic numerals? Because the Arabs brought them to Europe, around the year A.D. 1000, when they ruled
8 Spain. The Arabs, however, called these digits Hindu numerals, because they had borrowed them from India.

It's hard to believe that for most of their time on Earth, humans had no numbers. How would our life today be different without counting? The list of ways is, well…infinite!

GUIDED QUESTIONS

7 **Link ideas to your own experience and knowledge:** Have you ever used Roman numerals? What is your opinion of them, as a counting system?

8 **Summarize** what you've learned from the article. (Hey, that's the extended-response question, isn't it?)

Go on to the next page

READING GUIDE

Sample Extended-Response Question

9 **1.** Summarize the history of counting, as told in the article.

GUIDED QUESTIONS

9 **Notice the key word, *summarize*. Remember to include only important information.**

Activity

Directions Write your answer to the extended-response question on the lines provided under the question.

Self-Evaluation

Ask yourself:

- Did I use my time wisely by planning my answer?
- Did I stick to the topic and avoid straying?
- Is my answer well-organized?
- Did I use transitions to make connections clearer?

How Your Response Will Be Evaluated

Your response will be evaluated on a scale of 0-4, using the rubric below. Read the rubric, and make sure you understand it, so that you will understand what the scorers of your test will be looking for.

Extended-Response Rubric

Score	Description
4	• Provides extensive evidence of the kind of interpretation called for in the item or question • Is well organized, elaborate, and thorough • Demonstrates a complete understanding of the whole work as well as how the parts blend to form the whole • Is relevant, comprehensive, and detailed, demonstrating a thorough understanding of the reading selection • Thoroughly addresses the important elements of the question • Contains logical reasoning and communicates effectively and clearly *(A four-point response may go beyond the requirements of the item.)*
3	• Provides evidence that essential interpretation has been made • Is thoughtful and reasonably accurate • Indicates an understanding of the concept or item • Communicates adequately, and generally reaches reasonable conclusions • Contains some combination of the following flaws: ◆ Minor flaws in reasoning or interpretation ◆ Failure to address some aspect of the item or omission of some detail
2	• Is mostly accurate and relevant • Contains some combination of the following flaws: ◆ Incomplete evidence of interpretation ◆ Unsubstantiated statements made about the text ◆ Incomplete understanding of the concept or item ◆ Lack of comprehensiveness, faulty reasoning, unclear communication

<table>
<tr><td>1</td><td>

- Provides little evidence of interpretation
- Is unorganized and incomplete
- Exhibits decoding rather than reading
- Demonstrates a partial understanding of the item, but is sketchy and unclear
- Indicates some effort beyond restating the item
- Contains some combination of the following flaws:
  - Little understanding of the concept or item
  - Failure to address most aspects of the item
  - Inability to make coherent meaning from the text

</td></tr>
</table>

0	• Shows no understanding of the item or student fails to respond to item

Question

Summarize the history of counting, as told in the article.

Sample Response

The earliest counting devices that have been discovered so far are notched bones made by Middle Eastern hunting and gathering peoples about fifteen thousand years ago. The notches are very simple-one follows another, each one is like the next, and they are not grouped. The people who made the notches may not have had numbers; their counting may have consisted only of "another and another and another..." Then, ten to five thousand years ago, farming peoples developed a system of tokens made for counting items, such as sheep or jars of oil. However, each type of item was

represented by a different type of counter. This made sense for farming people who were counting their goods, but it made for a concrete number system rather than an abstract one. In an abstract number system, numbers are things in themselves. They are separate from the things they count. One is one, for example, and it may represent one sheep or one jar. Abstract numbers were invented by the Sumerians about five thousand years ago. However, the Sumerian system lacked a zero. Our system, which we call "Arabic numbers," was brought to medieval Spain by the Arabs; but the Arabs in turn had learned it from India, and called the system "Hindu numbers."

Evaluation

This response earns a 4, the highest score. In summarizes all the important information in the article, in detail. It is well organized—it follows time order—and well written. It includes a knowledgeable discussion of abstract and concrete numbers, and shows an understanding of the practical reasons why counting was invented.

Activity

Directions Evaluate your own extended response to the question. Use the rubric. Write your evaluation on the lines below.

Proofreading Practice

Make sure you proofread your extended response before handing in your test. When you proofread, you look over your writing for even the smallest errors, and you correct them.

- grammar
- spelling
- punctuation
- capitalization

Activity

Directions The passage below contains errors. Correct them all. Change wordings when necessary.

Counting! An important topic since anceint times. The first counting marks we've found were nachos on bone. They were made by people about 15000 years ago. Later, the sumerians starting using tokens for counting, one kind of token might be used for a sheep and some other kind for a jar. They were farmers. Later, some other guys in Iraq invented abstrat numbers. The number was the same no matter what kind of thing you were counting. But they didn't have zero. Like no zeros in 24,51 (204,501). Greek, Roman, and Arabic numbers came later, which is really Hindu numbers.

Read the selection and answer the questions.

Say Hey!
Who's the Best?
By Robert E. Hood

Many fans think that Willie Mays was the greatest baseball player of all time. They might be right.

Willie Mays was the Michael Jordan of baseball–30 years before Mike hit the NBA basketball court.

Mays could hit a ball often and far. A wizard in center field, he had wide range, incredible instincts and a laser-like throwing arm. He ran the bases like an express train. He could do anything on the ball field, and he did it with style and a grin that ignited the fans.

The finest all-round player of his time–and maybe of all time–he also was the most exciting.

Big, Big, Numbers

Mays was the first great slugger to steal more than 30 bases and hit more than 30 homers in a season. He was the first to steal more than 300 bases and hit more than 300 homers in a career. And he was the first National League player to hit more than 600 home runs in a career.

Speed and power, he had both. He could score from first base on a single. Once he hit four homers in a game. Few players, if any, have done both. For 22 year, Willie Mays awed fans with his artistry and his joyous play.

Superb Athlete

Born in the small town of Westfield, Ala., Willie Howard Mays took to baseball early. Before he could walk he was playing with a large ball his father gave him.

Willie's dad was an outstanding semi-pro ballplayer, and his son loved to watch him. Soon Willie too was excelling at the game, hitting the ball farther and throwing it harder than his playmates.

A superb athlete in high school, he starred in football, with his blistering speed and powerful passing arm. In basketball, he led all players in the county in scoring.

He could have gone to college on a scholarship, but chose baseball as a career. At age 16, in 1947, he signed a contract to play for the Birmingham Black Barons in the Negro League. Becoming a professional meant he could no longer play high school sports. But he continued his studies until he received his diploma.

We Are the Champions

Mays developed into a sensational player with the Black Barons, and in 1950 caught the eye of the major-league New York Giants. After tearing up the minor leagues, Mays was called up to the Giants in 1951.

He had become a major-leaguer in less than two years, and would help the Giants win their first pennant since 1937.

His favorite expression, "Say, Hey," earned him the nickname of the Say Hey Kid. His bubbly manner and high-pitched laughter caused teammates to treat him like a good-luck charm.

Willie's key hits and big plays inspired the Giants to win the pennant from the Brooklyn Dodgers in a dramatic playoff.

Mays served in the Army in 1952 and 1953, and without him the Giants became an also-ran team.

He returned for the 1954 season, and manager Leo Durocher stated: "He means the pennant to us. This year I figure he'll bat .280 and hit 25 homers."

Durocher was wrong. Mays did far better, leading the National League with .345 average and hitting 41 home runs. The Giants won the pennant and beat the Cleveland Indians in four straight in the World Series.

The Catch of All Time

In the first game of the Series, Mays made the incredible catch that turns up every year on television replays. In the eighth inning with the score tied, Cleveland put two men on base. Up came Vic Wertz, who hit a tremendous drive to deepest center field. Willie turned his back and streaked to the faraway fence. Catching the ball over his shoulder, he whirled and uncorked a bullet-like throw to the infield. This prevented a run from scoring, and the Giants went on to win in the 10th inning.

In 1958, the New York Giants became the San Francisco Giants. Moving west didn't dim Mays's brilliance. Over his career, he would appear in 24 All-Star Games.

Hall of Famer Ted Williams said it best: "They ***invented*** the All-Star Game for Willie."

Go On

1. Willie Mays was one of the greatest ________ players of all time.

   A. football

   B. basketball

   C. baseball

   D. tennis

2. What was the key to Mays' athletic greatness?

   A. He hit more home runs than anyone else.

   B. He was the fastest pitcher of his time.

   C. He was a friendly, exciting player.

   D. He was an all-around player who excelled at hitting, running, and fielding.

3. Why did Mays have to stop playing high school sports in 1947?

   A. He joined the army.

   B. It was against the law in his state for African-American students to be on teams.

   C. He became a professional athlete in that year, at age 16.

   D. That was the year he graduated.

4. What expression is Willie Mays best known for?

   A. "Say, Hey!"

   B. "Let's play a double-header!"

   C. "I never met a man I didn't like."

   D. "I don't care what they throw, I can hit it."

5. One of Mays' great plays is shown again and again on television replays. What is it?

   A. a catch and throw in deep center field in the World Series

   B. a strikeout in a crucial ninth inning

   C. winning the pennant in 1952

   D. hitting more than 600 home runs in his career

6. Choose a great athlete of today, such as Tiger Woods, Mark McGwire, or Venus Williams (or her sister Serena!). Compare and contrast that athlete to Willie Mays. Include at least one comparison and one contrast.

   ____

   ____

   ____

   ____

7. Suppose you are telling a friend about Willie Mays, in your own words. Below, write down what you would say.

   ____

   ____

   ____

   ____

   ____

   ____

   ____

   ____

   ____

Workshop

Choose Materials

1. Think of a nonfiction subject that you are interested in. Look in the catalog of your library for books on that subject. Write the titles and authors of at least six such books on the lines below.

____

____

____

____

____

____

2. Imagine that you are writing a report on one of the nonfiction topics below. Your purpose is to develop your own ideas and interpretations based on information in your sources. Choose your topic from the list. Then, in your library, find three sources of information on that topic. One source should be a book, one should be a magazine or newspaper article, and the third should be in a nonprint medium such as CD, CD-ROM, Web site, videotape, audiotape, or phonograph record. List the *best* source you can find in each of the three media.

- visual art
- cultures of Asia or Africa
- history of the United States before 1900
- one sport of your choice
- a twentieth-century invention of your choice
- latest theories about a childhood illness
- exploring outer space
- a man or woman in the news
- opportunities to make money in today's world

Home Involvement Activities

Reading Activity

When you read a good book, share it with others! After each member of your family reads a book, ask that person to fill out a book card. Make book cards out of index cards and keep them in a flip-top box such as a recipe card holder. On each card, write the following information:

Title of the book ______________________________

Author(s) ______________________________

Date Read ______________________________

What It Was About ______________________________

____

____

____

____

What I Learned ______________________________

____

____

____

____

Would I Recommend It to Someone Else? ______________

____

Why? ______________________________

____

____

After you finish reading each book, share your reactions to it with your family.

Speaking and Listening Activity

Form a group with one or more people who share your interest in reading nonfiction, or in some specific nonfiction topic. Decide on a book to read. Set a time and place to discuss the book, perhaps one week from when you choose the book. Have a good discussion! Set forth your ideas and responses, listen to others', and comment constructively.

Viewing Activity

There's a lot of good nonfiction on television. Documentaries and news are two prime sources. Whether it's the biography of a past leader, an interview with a famous writer, a special about a trouble spot far away, a night of coverage of a political convention, or a wildlife documentary, you can expand your horizons by choosing the best of televised nonfiction. Find a program that interests you. Watch it carefully and critically, taking notes. Then, write a critical evaluation, about half a page long. Share it by reading aloud to classmates.

Notes

Notes

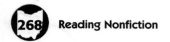

Notes

Notes

Notes

Notes

Notes

Notes

Notes

Notes

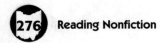